REPROGRAMMING
THE OVERWEIGHT MIND™

Disclaimer Notice:

Mention of specific companies, organizations, or authorities does not imply an endorsement by the publisher, nor does mention of specific companies, organizations, or authorities imply they endorse this Workbook.

The author and publisher shall have neither liability nor responsibility to any person or entity with respect to any loss or damage caused or alleged to be caused, directly or indirectly, by the information contained in this Work Journal.

Making multiple Copies of this copyrighted document and its Subconscious Restructuring™ trademark for distribution purposes is strictly forbidden. This includes but is not limited to counselors, coaches, and mental health professionals who make copies for their clients. Only SR™ Practitioners are licensed to print multiple copies for their clients only.

CONTENT

INTRODUCTION

What Do Weight Control, Anorexia, Bulimia, and Binge Eating Have in Common

What weight control, anorexia, bulimia, and binge eating have in common is one's emotional state and gut health. Regardless of what initiated the disruptions in the emotional state and microbiota (gut health), it becomes a self-perpetuating mechanism if both are not measured, tracked and improved simultaneously. This is why Reprogramming The Overweight Mind begins with an Emotional Fitness Checklist and then breaks down the components of thought, emotion, and behavior, which empowers you to interrupt, restructure, and reprogram any unwanted behavior.

The Gut Health Variable

When I speak of the gut, I am referring to the approximately 27 feet of intestines between the esophagus and rectum. This part of the body is known as the enteric nervous system (ENS), is lined with approximately five hundred million neurons (brain cells), and has bidirectional communication with the main brain (the one between your ears), primarily through the vagus nerve. This is why some refer to the gut as the second brain.

The microbiota is simply the microbial taxa associated with humans that enable gut-brain communication. There are many different ways the microbiota can become disrupted, which in turn can and will affect your emotional state. The questions on the Gut Health Checklist are symptoms that can arise from a disrupted microbiota. You will want to keep in mind anything from the gut health checklist that may be an issue for you and make it a health objective.

The text on the Step 6 page breaks down multiple gut health mechanisms, including oxalate poisoning, candida, bile sludge, microbiota disruption, mitochondrial dysfunction, and how to correct it. It also includes the tools you will need to get started. The vast majority of MDs, even functional medicine MDs, are unaware of these mechanisms, so feel free to give your MD a copy of this book and let them read it over. Engaging in "Cracking the Gut Health Code" requires the integration of a Functional Medicine MD.

With over half a billion neurons (brain cells) in the gut, it can literally dictate what you are thinking. This is why Step 6 breaks down these mechanisms and how to correct them to regain synchronicity between the two brains. Step 6 is designed to educate you and your MD on the fundamental tests and gut health mechanisms to move forward in this relatively new landscape.

The intestinal microbiome (the cumulative genetic material of the intestinal microbiota) is a complex network of over twenty-two million unique microbial genes that contribute to critical host functions such as digestion and absorption of calories from the gut. The impact of short and long-term diets on the composition of the gut microbiome has been reported, and the relationship between this microbial community and adiposity is well-documented; however, gut microbiota-host interactions have recently become a focus of psychopathology. Over the past decade, gut microbiota-based studies have reported compelling evidence that this complex microbial community regulates anxiety and stress-related behavior.

Additionally, consistent evidence has also identified the gut microbiota as a key regulator of pathways (neurobiological, immune, and inflammatory) associated with the gut-brain axis—a track for bidirectional communication between the central and enteric nervous systems [14].

Gut health cannot be ignored if you want to change any behavior permanently.

Subconscious Restructuring™: A Profound Paradigm Shift in Disordered Eating

Subconscious Restructuring™ (SR™) is Evidence-Based Emotional Health designed to interrupt, restructure, and reprogram one's thoughts, emotions, and behavior without meds, labels, or personal history.

SR™ does not depend on your personal history, labeling, or observational, subjective assessment to fix or improve behavior. SR™ goes straight to the problem and immediately to the fix.

What is the Function of Conscious & Subconscious?

The conscious mind has a single function: to deliver information to the subconscious; the subconscious does everything else.

There is a consistent process the subconscious must go through for an emotional state and behavior to come about. One is subject to the random and autonomic processes of the subconscious if one needs help understanding how it works and how to interrupt, restructure, and reprogram it.

How the Subconscious Works and How to Take Control of It

Everything you have ever seen, heard, felt, tasted, or smelled has been stored in your subconscious since your first breath. The subconscious uses this information to determine how you emotionally respond to your world, which in turn will equal your behavior. One must fully understand how the subconscious works and how to take control of it, including the tools to interrupt, restructure, and reprogram the subconscious if something is determined not to work.

Will SR™ Help Me Manage, Modify, or Cope?

SR™ is designed for a complete, positive, empowered change. It simply does not make sense to modify, manage, or cope with something that does not work. It does make sense to interrupt a process that does not work before it begins, then restructure and reprogram it to produce a different emotional response and permanently change an unwanted behavior.

What is the foundation of SR™?

One's emotional state is the single constant of all human behavior; in other words, your emotional state = your behavior. How you feel about everything you do will always determine whether you move toward it. You will always move toward perceived pleasure and away from pain. This is why Step 1 of SR™ is a three-instrument checklist beginning with an Emotional Checklist.

The Power of Your Subconscious

To give you an idea of the power of your subconscious, you can speak at a rate of about two to three hundred words per minute. Your subconscious runs at a rate of about one thousand to twelve hundred words per minute, which is about four times faster than you can speak. This is why you can talk on the phone and perform other tasks like typing on the computer or driving a car because the subconscious is already programmed to do the other tasks.

When a single objective comes to mind, it is like a tug of war with a vat of mud in the middle for whoever loses. Your single objective is one person on one side against the subconscious, which is four people on the other side. If one does not understand how to interrupt, restructure, and reprogram the subconscious, one will be subject to the autonomic processes of the subconscious.

Interrupt – Restructure – Reprogram

If you are having a negative or destructive response to subconscious information, how then do you **Interrupt**, **Restructure,** and **Reprogram** this? Once you understand the basics, you can begin taking control at the beginning of the process.

You must understand how to take control of your subconscious because it is like a car without an off switch and an unknown driver if you do not predetermine the destination. If you decide not to drive, or at least tell the driver where you are going, it is going to drive itself, or someone else will get in the seat and drive it for you. Someone else driving might be okay if you agree to where they are going, but what if you do not?

Most parents do not realize they are programming their children from the very moment they enter the world, and they are just passing along what their parents have taught them, good or bad. A tremendous number of variables can occur in your initial programming, which may have little to do with your parents. The bottom line remains. Do you want to drive at some point, or do you want to continue letting someone or something else drive?

Interrupt

The core issue with all behavior that does not work is that you are emotionally out of control, and you must decide if you want to interrupt this process. Someone who has spent two, five, ten years or more trying to fix a problem will usually consider it arrogant of anyone, particularly a psychologist or psychiatrist, to tell them what they need to do. Telling someone to change will never equal empowering them with the tools to consistently interrupt a process, which does not work.

Does This Work for Me?

If you ask yourself the first key question from Step 5 daily (Does this work for me?), you will recognize what you need to interrupt. After you recognize what you need to interrupt, you write this down as your initial objective.

Restructure

You can begin the restructuring process after interrupting a thought, emotion, and behavior that does not work. There is only one way to do this effectively, and that is to have an organized process to put the subconscious on paper or online.

You must document everything. If you do not, how do you know where you have started, where you are going, or where you have ended up? Without documenting this information, you are guessing. Simply put, you cannot effect change in anything unless you take action.

Gaining access to the subconscious begins with establishing your objective. The next step is to document how you relate to this objective or communicate with yourself about it. Talking to yourself is the first component of information, which determines your emotional state and behavior, and it is important to find out how you speak to yourself regarding an objective.

Access to subconscious information is afforded by simply responding to four statements and one question about your objectives or objectives. This is known as the Subconscious Perspective and is Step 2 of SR™.

Reprogram

Once you understand how to interrupt and restructure subconscious information, which does not work, the process of reprogramming is relatively simple. We say relatively because sometimes the most powerful program you may need to overcome is the program to allow the subconscious to run itself.

You must consistently evaluate your self-talk and determine whether it is a dialogue that is going to lead you to an objective or objective you have chosen. If not, you must consistently interrupt this process and restructure it until you have reprogrammed yourself, which will move you in a predetermined direction.

Defining Normal with the Emotional Fitness Checklist™

One's emotional state is the single constant of all human behavior or disordered behavior. It simply makes sense to 'Define Normal' with the Emotional Fitness Checklist™ because emotion drives behavior. Neither the mental health system nor the DSM offer a clear definition of 'Normal.'

- The Emotional Fitness Checklist™ is used to 'Define Normal.'
- Emotional and Behavioral Objectives are Absolutely Clear when you 'Define Normal.'
- When you 'Define Normal,' you can 'Define Better.'
- Emotional and Behavioral Objectives are accomplished with Subconscious Restructuring®.

Reasons to Define Normal with Emotional Measurement™

When ambiguous behaviors are used in psychological assessments, anyone can be diagnosed with a behavior disorder and subject to endless experimentation with dangerous pharmaceuticals. When Emotional Measurement™ is used to 'Define, Normal' behavioral medications for adults and children are virtually eliminated, which will lower the risk of suicide, heart attack, and sudden death. Physiological disorders are more easily detected with a definition of normal.

One must 'Define Normal' with Emotional Measurement™ if one expects to have an accurate diagnosis, have the ability to track progress over time, monitor the proficiency of a Practitioner, and establish the efficacy of a treatment.

Normal Range for the Burris Institute Emotional Fitness 3 Instrument 22 Point Checklist

Emotional Checklist: 1 – 4

Behavior Control Checklist: 7 – 10

Relationship Satisfaction Scale: 7 -10

*All instruments are based on a scale of 1-10

Defining Evidence-Based: Show Me the Data

Many people in the emotional health (mental health) industry claim evidence-based, yet they can not produce any evidence when asked. The reason they will give for not showing any evidence is client practitioner confidentiality. This is when you remind them that you did not ask for personal client information. You only want to see the outcomes in the form of measurable data from the client. In my opinion, if you cannot produce any evidence, you cannot claim evidence-based. All SR™ Practitioners are required to measure emotional and gut health at every session.

Producing client data is only part of the equation. The other part of the equation is the meaning the data has. This is why three simple questions must be asked when evaluating client data.

3 KQs (Key Questions) Define Evidence-Based

KQ1. What is measured?

KQ2. Why is it measured?

KQ3. How are the outcomes generated?

Following are answers that are specific to the Subconscious Restructuring™ paradigm. Regardless of the modality, however, these three KQs must be clearly answered if there is a claim of evidence-based or measurable outcomes.

Answers

KQ 1: What is measured?

Emotional Checklist: The 12-point Emotional Checklist consists of a full range of human emotions and issues to collectively indicate a depressed state. There are also individual questions within the Emotional Checklist, which address specific issues. The first three questions indicate anxiety, negative self-talk, and anger levels. These are the first three issues addressed through the initial four-hour, seven-step process of Subconscious Restructuring™. Question 4 addresses sleep, and question 5 addresses sadness and hopelessness. Question 9 is regarding eating behavior, and question 12 addresses suicidal ideation.

Behavior Control Checklist: The 5-point Behavior Control Checklist enables the client to grade the practitioner regarding the delivery of information and the client's ability to comprehend the process. The practitioner can then address those issues if the numbers do not adequately come up.

Relationship Satisfaction Scale: The 5-point Relationship Satisfaction Scale addresses how the client relates to the people they are closest to in their lives. The Relationship Satisfaction Scale measures how one communicates with people closest to them and how satisfied they are with those relationships.

KQ 2: Why is it Measured?

Depression: The proportion of the global population living with depression is estimated to be 322 million people, and it is the leading cause of disability worldwide [1].

People who have depression along with another medical illness tend to have more severe symptoms of both depression and the medical illness, more difficulty adapting to their medical condition, and more medical costs than those who do not have co-existing depression [2].

Treating depression can help improve the outcome of treating co-occurring illnesses. About one in 10 Americans aged 12 and over takes antidepressant medication [5].

Anxiety: anxiety disorders are the most common class of mental disorders, with a 12-month prevalence rate of 24.9% [3]. Women are 60% more likely than men to experience an anxiety disorder over their lifetime. Non-Hispanic blacks are 20% less likely, and Hispanics are 30% less likely than non-Hispanic whites to experience an anxiety disorder during their lifetime. An extensive national survey of adolescent mental health reported that about 8 percent of teens ages 13–18 have an anxiety disorder, with symptoms commonly emerging around age 6 [5].

Negative Self-Talk: It is the strength of predominantly negative self-talk that predicts ED severity [6]. Automatic negative self-talk is linked to depression, anxiety, and other disorders in children [7]. The first component the subconscious uses to bring about an emotional state and behavior is an internal dialogue, and this is the first process to be interrupted, restructured, and reprogrammed with the Subconscious Restructuring™ process.

Anger: Anger and hostility are linked to coronary heart disease in both healthy and CHD populations [8].

Sleep: A chronic sleep-restricted state can cause fatigue, daytime sleepiness, clumsiness, and weight loss or weight gain [9]. Sleep deprivation adversely affects the brain and cognitive function [10].

Eating Behavior: Physiological changes as a result of disordered eating can affect psychology, and in turn, the psychology that brings about disordered eating affects physiology [11].

Suicidal Ideation: Suicidal ideation has been linked to hopelessness and anxiety [12] , both of which are measured in the Emotional Checklist. Question 12 is a straightforward indicator of suicidal ideation and many times closely correlates with question 1 (anxiety) and question 5 (hopelessness). The risk of suicide attempts among the PTSD population is six times greater than in the general population [13].

KQ 3: How is the Data Generated?

The client generates subconscious Restructuring™ data. The client or practitioner cannot change this data after it is saved.

References

1. Friedrich M. Depression Is the Leading Cause of Disability Around the World. JAMA. 2017;317(15):1517. doi:10.1001/jama.2017.3826

2. Herrera PA, Campos-Romero S, Szabo W, Martínez P, Guajardo V, Rojas G. Understanding the Relationship between Depression and Chronic Diseases Such as Diabetes and Hypertension: A Grounded Theory Study. Int J Environ Res Public Health. 2021 Nov 19;18(22):12130. doi: 10.3390/ijerph182212130. PMID: 34831886; PMCID: PMC8618720.

3. Bandelow B, Michaelis S. Epidemiology of anxiety disorders in the 21st century. Dialogues Clin Neurosci. 2015 Sep;17(3):327-35. doi: 10.31887/DCNS.2015.17.3/bbandelow. PMID: 26487813; PMCID: PMC4610617.

4. Antidepressant Use in Persons Aged 12 and Over: United States, 2005–2008: http://www.cdc.gov/nchs/data/databriefs/db76.htm

5. Anxiety: Who is at Risk https://www.nimh.nih.gov/health/topics/anxiety-disorders/index.shtml#par...

6. Scott N, Hanstock TL, Thornton C. Dysfunctional self-talk associated with eating disorder severity and symptomatology. J Eat Disord. 2014;2:14.

7. Hogendoorn SM, Wolters LH, Vervoort L, et al. Measuring Negative and Positive Thoughts in Children: An Adaptation of the Children's Automatic Thoughts Scale (CATS). Cognit Ther Res. 2010;34(5):467-478.

8. Chida Y, Steptoe A. The association of anger and hostility with future coronary heart disease: a meta-analytic review of prospective evidence. J Am Coll Cardiol. 2009;53(11):936-46.

9. Taheri S, Lin L, Austin D, Young T, Mignot E. Short sleep duration is associated with reduced leptin, elevated ghrelin, and increased body mass index. PLoS Med. 2004;1(3):e62.

10. Hsieh S, Li TH, Tsai LL. Impact of monetary incentives on cognitive performance and error monitoring following sleep deprivation. Sleep. 2010;33(4):499-507.

11. Vögele C, Florin I. Psychophysiological responses to food exposure: an experimental study in binge eaters. Int J Eat Disord. 1997;21(2):147-57.

12. Beck AT, Brown GK, Steer RA, Dahlsgaard KK, Grisham JR. Suicide ideation at its worst point: a predictor of eventual suicide in psychiatric outpatients. Suicide Life Threat Behav. 1999;29(1):1-9.

13. Sher L. Suicide in war veterans: the role of comorbidity of PTSD and depression. Expert Rev Neurother. 2009;9(7):921-3.

14. Reed KK, Abbaspour A, Bulik CM, Carroll IM. The intestinal microbiota and anorexia nervosa: cause or consequence of nutrient deprivation. Curr Opin Endocr Metab Res. 2021 Aug;19:46-51. doi: 10.1016/j.coemr.2021.06.003. Epub 2021 Jun 17. PMID: 34458645; PMCID: PMC8386495.

THE EMOTIONAL FITNESS CHECKLIST

To effectively address the behavior you want to change, you need to establish a foundation that will enable you to address the specifics of what you wish to change. This is why SR™ works for everyone because it establishes a solid emotional foundation from which to work.

SR™ is broken down into 7 Steps and covers the full range of emotions and human behavior. This is necessary if you want to affect any single issue.

You cannot get control unless you start by understanding how you talk to yourself, how you feel, and your perception of the world. The big question when attempting to initiate any change in your life is. Where do you start? A simple answer would be at the beginning. The next question would be. Where is the beginning? The beginning is to find out how you feel on a sliding scale. This is another troubling issue about going to a psychologist or psychiatrist. You sit there talking while the psychologist or psychiatrist is writing things down. The question is. "Shouldn't you be the one writing?" The answer to this is an emphatic "Yes."

The Emotional Fitness Checklist has three sections; the first is the **Emotional Checklist**. This section will help you understand how you are doing emotionally right now and the areas you need to give the most attention. The second is the **Behavior Control Checklist**. This section is designed to establish how well you understand your subconscious and the process of SR™. The third section is the **Relationship Satisfaction Scale**. This is important because if you are speaking negatively to yourself, this will carry through to how you speak to others. Good people skills will always outweigh intelligence, and the Relationship Satisfaction Scale will ensure your people skills are in check.

EMOTIONAL FITNESS CHECKLIST

Name_____Date of Birth_____Age____Sex_____Today's Date_____

Please write a score of 1-10 after each question

Not at all	Somewhat	Moderately	A Lot
1	5	10	

EMOTIONAL CHECKLIST	
1) Do you worry about family, friends, self, events, future, etc.?	
2) Do you get self-critical and blame yourself for everything?	
3) Have you been feeling resentful or angry?	
4) Do you find it hard to get a good night's sleep?	
5) Have you been feeling sad, or do you feel your future is hopeless?	
6) Do you feel inferior to others or think of yourself as a failure?	
7) Have you lost interest in your career, hobby, family, or friends?	
8) Do you feel overwhelmed and have to push yourself hard to do things?	
9) Have you lost your appetite, or do you compulsively overeat?	
10) Do you have trouble making up your mind?	
11) Do you have feelings of hatred toward anyone, anything, or yourself?	
12) Do you feel life is not worth living?	
Total	

BEHAVIOR CONTROL CHECKLIST	
1) How would you rate your understanding of how the subconscious works?	
2) How would you rate your ability to restructure subconscious processes?	
3) Please rate your ability to maintain your most powerful emotional state.	
4) How would you rate your confidence in achieving your objectives?	
5) How would you rate your self-motivation and ability to stay focused?	
Total	

RELATIONSHIP SATISFACTION SCALE	
1) How would you rate your communication with people closest to you?	
2) Resolving conflicts and arguments with people closest to you?	
3) Satisfaction with your role in the relationships of the people closest to you?	
4) Satisfaction with the other people's role in your relationships?	
5) Love for people closest to you?	
Total	

EMOTIONAL FITNESS CHECKLIST

Name_____Date of Birth_____Age____Sex_____Today's Date_____

Please write a score of 1-10 after each question

Not at all	Somewhat	Moderately	A Lot
1	5	10	

EMOTIONAL CHECKLIST

1) Do you worry about family, friends, self, events, future, etc.?	
2) Do you get self-critical and blame yourself for everything?	
3) Have you been feeling resentful or angry?	
4) Do you find it hard to get a good night's sleep?	
5) Have you been feeling sad, or do you feel your future is hopeless?	
6) Do you feel inferior to others or think of yourself as a failure?	
7) Have you lost interest in your career, hobby, family, or friends?	
8) Do you feel overwhelmed and have to push yourself hard to do things?	
9) Have you lost your appetite, or do you compulsively overeat?	
10) Do you have trouble making up your mind?	
11) Do you have feelings of hatred toward anyone, anything, or yourself?	
12) Do you feel life is not worth living?	
Total	

BEHAVIOR CONTROL CHECKLIST

1) How would you rate your understanding of how the subconscious works?	
2) How would you rate your ability to restructure subconscious processes?	
3) Please rate your ability to maintain your most powerful emotional state.	
4) How would you rate your confidence in achieving your objectives?	
5) How would you rate your self-motivation and ability to stay focused?	
Total	

RELATIONSHIP SATISFACTION SCALE

1) How would you rate your communication with people closest to you?	
2) Resolving conflicts and arguments with people closest to you?	
3) Satisfaction with your role in the relationships of the people closest to you?	
4) Satisfaction with the other people's role in your relationships?	
5) Love for people closest to you?	
Total	

EMOTIONAL FITNESS CHECKLIST

Name_____Date of Birth_____Age____Sex_____Today's Date_____

Please write a score of 1-10 after each question

Not at all	Somewhat	Moderately	A Lot
1	5	10	

EMOTIONAL CHECKLIST	
1) Do you worry about family, friends, self, events, future, etc.?	
2) Do you get self-critical and blame yourself for everything?	
3) Have you been feeling resentful or angry?	
4) Do you find it hard to get a good night's sleep?	
5) Have you been feeling sad, or do you feel your future is hopeless?	
6) Do you feel inferior to others or think of yourself as a failure?	
7) Have you lost interest in your career, hobby, family, or friends?	
8) Do you feel overwhelmed and have to push yourself hard to do things?	
9) Have you lost your appetite, or do you compulsively overeat?	
10) Do you have trouble making up your mind?	
11) Do you have feelings of hatred toward anyone, anything, or yourself?	
12) Do you feel life is not worth living?	
Total	

BEHAVIOR CONTROL CHECKLIST	
1) How would you rate your understanding of how the subconscious works?	
2) How would you rate your ability to restructure subconscious processes?	
3) Please rate your ability to maintain your most powerful emotional state?	
4) How would you rate your confidence in achieving your objectives?	
5) How would you rate your self-motivation and ability to stay focused?	
Total	

RELATIONSHIP SATISFACTION SCALE	
1) How would you rate your communication with people closest to you?	
2) Resolving conflicts and arguments with people closest to you?	
3) Satisfaction with your role in the relationships of the people closest to you?	
4) Satisfaction with the other people's role in your relationships?	
5) Love for people closest to you?	
Total	

What Does Your Score Mean

You have now established a baseline so you can begin to identify areas that need the most work. Before accurately assessing yourself, you must put yourself through the SR™ process and then fill out another Emotional Fitness Checklist without looking at the first Emotional Fitness Checklist you just filled out.

The Emotional Checklist: Your objective is the lowest score possible. If any of your responses are 4 or lower, we consider this a normal range, and there is no significant need for concern, but you need to address it and try to bring the number down even further. If any of your responses are a 5 or above, you need to monitor this issue and restructure the subconscious processes that may keep this number high. A sustained score of 5 or above on question 12 indicates you need to work with an SR™ Practitioner. If question 12 remains at a 5 or above with the SR™ Practitioner, they will refer you to a physician or psychiatrist. The total score on all these is less important than the individual scores.

The Behavior Control Checklist: Your objective here is the highest score possible, with the normal range being a 7 - 10. It is essential to try to score yourself accurately. If you **think** you know how your subconscious works, this is a lot different than **knowing** how your subconscious works. You will know how your subconscious works after putting yourself through the SR™ process; therefore, your score will improve.

Relationship Satisfaction Scale: Your objective here is the highest score possible, with the normal range being a 7 - 10. The first component of information that determines your emotional state and behavior is how you speak to yourself. When you restructure how you speak to yourself, it is reflected when you speak to others. This will raise your score in this area as well.

After you have completed the 7 Step SR™ process, you will want to do another Checklist within 24 hours. After that, a minimum of once a week for one month. The length of time you stay with the program depends on how significant the changes you need to make are and your age and gender. The bottom line is the program process of SR™ conforms to how the subconscious works, and it will be up to you to continue to implement the tools you have learned until you achieve the exact results you want.

With a free account at BurrisConnect.com, you can access Step 1 and Step 6 forms. This includes a color-coded progress tracker.

SUBCONSCIOUS PERSPECTIVE & EMPOWERING QUESTIONS

Before we start on the Subconscious Perspective, we need to define where you want to be emotionally, spiritually, and physically (mind-body-spirit). To do this, please choose where you want to be on a scale of 1-10.

Emotional Spiritual Physical Scale

Males		Females	
10	This is a pro athlete or performer territory, and your trainer and MD will establish these parameters.	10	This is a pro athlete or performer territory, and your trainer and MD will establish these parameters.
9	**Emotional**: Express love and kindness to yourself and others at every opportunity **Spiritual**: Meditate as you get up each morning and as you go to bed each night with a focus on objectives. **Physical**: Consistent Structured Lifting and Aerobic Program Physical & NutrVal Every Year, plus other recommended labs **Diet**: Flexible Carnivore Intermittent and Extended Fasting No Sugar, Alcohol, or Caffeine **Body Fat**: 10 to 12%	9	**Emotional**: Express love and kindness to yourself and others at every opportunity **Spiritual**: Meditate as you get up each morning and as you go to bed each night with a focus on objectives. **Physical**: Consistent Structured Lifting and Aerobic Program Physical & NutrVal Every Year, plus other recommended labs **Diet**: Flexible Carnivore Intermittent and Extended Fasting No Sugar, Alcohol, or Caffeine **Body Fat**: 15 to 17%

Emotional Spiritual Physical Scale

Males		Females	
8	**Emotional**: Express love and kindness to yourself and others at every opportunity **Spiritual**: Meditate as you get up each morning and as you go to bed each night with a center on objectives **Physical**: Consistent Structured Lifting and Aerobic Program **Diet**: Flexible Carnivore Intermittent and Extended Fasting **Body Fat**: 12 to 14% 2 Drinks per month 1 Regular or Decaff Coffee Per Day 3 Sugar foods per year	8	**Emotional**: Express love and kindness to yourself and others at every opportunity **Spiritual**: Meditate as you get up each morning and as you go to bed each night with a center on objectives **Physical**: Consistent Structured Lifting and Aerobic Program **Diet**: Flexible Carnivore Intermittent and Extended Fasting **Body Fat**: 17 to 19% 2 Drinks per month 1 Regular or Decaff Coffee Per Day 3 Sugar foods per year
7	**Emotional**: Express love and kindness to yourself and others but not consistently **Spiritual**: Meditate as you get up each morning and as you go to bed each night with a center on objectives **Physical**: You are experimenting with your exercise routine **Diet**: You are on a diet that has multiple cheat days per month Intermittent Fasting **Body Fat**: 14 to 16% 2 Drinks per week 2 Sugar foods per week	7	**Emotional**: Express love and kindness to yourself and others but not consistently **Spiritual**: Meditate as you get up each morning and as you go to bed each night with a center on objectives **Physical**: You are experimenting with your exercise routine **Diet**: You are on a diet that has multiple cheat days per month Intermittent Fasting **Body Fat**: 14 to 16% 2 Drinks per week 2 Sugar foods per week
6	**Emotional**: You begin to realize that love is absolute power but still struggle to connect. **Spiritual**: You meditate consistently 1 to 2 times per week	6	**Emotional**: You begin to realize that love is absolute power but still struggle to connect. **Spiritual**: You meditate consistently 1 to 2 times per week

	Physical: You begin an erratic walking program **Diet**: You take a hard look at what diet will improve your productivity **Body Fat**: 16 to 18% You begin to consider science-based protocols for objectives 4 Drinks per week 3 Sugar foods per week		**Physical**: You begin an erratic walking program **Diet**: You take a hard look at what diet will improve your productivity **Body Fat**: 21 to 23% You begin to consider science-based protocols for objectives 4 Drinks per week 3 Sugar foods per week

Emotional Spiritual Physical Scale

Males		Females	
5	**Emotional**: You occasionally express love but are not fully committed **Spiritual**: You do not take the opportunity to meditate for stress reduction and focus **Physical**: You consider a more refined diet and fitness options but still no structured protocol **Diet**: Flexible Carnivore **Body Fat**: 18 to 20%	**5**	**Emotional**: You occasionally express love but are not fully committed **Spiritual**: You do not take the opportunity to meditate for stress reduction and focus **Physical**: You consider a more refined diet and fitness options but still no structured protocol **Diet**: Flexible Carnivore **Body Fat**: 23 to 25%
4	**Emotional**: You express love and kindness occasionally, but it does not last **Spiritual**: You meditate occasionally when attending services **Physical**: You realize that alcohol and sugar are contributing to your ill health **Diet**: Too many carbohydrates and possible oxalate overload **Body Fat**: 20 to 22%	**4**	**Emotional**: You express love and kindness occasionally, but it does not last **Spiritual**: You meditate occasionally when attending services **Physical**: You realize that alcohol and sugar are contributing to your ill health **Diet**: Too many carbohydrates and possible oxalate overload **Body Fat**: 25 to 27%
3	**Emotional**: Express love and kindness, but it is, at best, erratic **Spiritual**: The relationship between the spiritual self not yet apparent **Physical**: You start weighing yourself and make haphazard attempts at dieting **Diet**: Starting to become cognizant of your poor eating and exercise habits **Body Fat**: 22 to 24%	**3**	**Emotional**: Express love and kindness, but it is, at best, erratic **Spiritual**: The relationship between the spiritual self not yet apparent **Physical**: You start weighing yourself and make haphazard attempts at dieting **Diet**: Starting to become cognizant of your poor eating and exercise habits **Body Fat**: 27 to 29%

Emotional Spiritual Physical Scale

Males		Females	
2	**Emotional**: Same as 1, but occasionally cognizant that you are not feeling well. **Spiritual**: Occasionally meditate when you need something **Physical**: You consider going to work as your exercise program. Nothing consistent or structured **Body Fat**: 24 to 26%	2	**Emotional**: Same as 1, but occasionally cognizant that you are not feeling well. **Spiritual**: Occasionally meditate when you need something **Physical**: You consider going to work as your exercise program. Nothing consistent or structured **Body Fat**: 29 to 31%
1	**Emotional**: Little, if any, Expression of love toward yourself or others **Spiritual**: Do not meditate **Physical**: You have no guidelines on how you treat your body or how fat and out of shape you are. **Diet**: You have no diet parameters **Body Fat**: 26 to 28% and beyond	1	**Emotional**: Little, if any, Expression of love toward yourself or others **Spiritual**: Do not meditate **Physical**: You have no guidelines on how you treat your body or how fat and out of shape you are **Diet**: You have no diet parameters **Body Fat**: 31 to 33% and beyond

Subconscious Perspective

In this section, you will put your subconscious on paper. There will be an introduction and an instruction set for each section. The Subconscious Perspective is 4 statements and one question you must respond to. This is about extracting and putting information from the subconscious on paper.

There are two keywords to keep in mind while writing down your objectives, and they are **ABSOLUTELY MUST**. Before you write down an objective, it needs to be clearly defined as an **ABSOLUTELY MUST,** just as you **ABSOLUTELY MUST** eat and drink to stay alive.

Following are questions for the **Subconscious Perspective**. These Questions will help you generate as much information as possible about each statement and question in the Subconscious Perspective. You can refer to this page as you fill out the Subconscious Perspective. You can go directly to the Subconscious Perspective form if you do not need these questions.

Subconscious Perspective: Objective Questions

1-A) Questions for Your Love Objectives
- Do I need to be more respectful and loving toward my family, myself, and others?
- Do I need to become more spiritually centered?

1-B) Questions for Your Health Objectives
- On a scale of 1-10, Where do I want my Emotional, Spiritual, and Physical health to be?
- Do I need to lose weight, increase my workout program, and improve my nutrition?

1-C) Questions for Your Wealth Objectives
- Do I need to manage my time better and increase my job satisfaction and purpose?
- Do I need to fulfill the divine design of my life?

1-D) Questions for Your Self-Image Objectives
- Do I need to improve my sense of humor and communication?
- Do I need to improve my self-confidence, self-esteem, and self-worth?

2) Questions for Your Reasons
- How will accomplishing my objectives affect my personal and professional relationships?
- Are there emotional, spiritual, and physical benefits for accomplishing my objectives?

3) Questions for What You ABSOLUTELY MUST Do to Accomplish Your Objectives
- Do I need to establish and maintain a flexible carnivore diet?
- Do I need a personal trainer to establish a consistent, structured fitness program?

Thinking of as many excuses as possible is crucial because you will learn how to use them to move more quickly toward your new objectives.

4) Questions for Your Excuses
- Do I use a friend, family member, work situation, time, or past failures as an excuse?
- Do I use any medical problems or cost and distance from the health club as an excuse?

Before responding to question 5, I need to ask you: Do you ask yourself questions? Yes. You ask yourself questions on an ongoing basis, and those questions begin as soon as you get up each morning. You ask questions like: "What do I need to do today?" *or* "What am I going to wear?" *or* "Whom do I need to call?" *or* "Where are my keys?"

5) A Question for Your Questions
A) If you do not ask yourself questions about your objectives, what questions would you ask yourself if you did?

After you have filled out the Subconscious Perspective, please go to the page after Empower Questions for an explanation of what you need to do next to initiate the process of restructuring your Subconscious Programming.

Subconscious Perspective & Empowering questions are on the following pages.

Subconscious Perspective: Objectives

1) Please write one objective per category you **ABSOLUTELY MUST** accomplish.

A) Love:
B) Health:
C) Wealth:
D) Self-Image:

2) Please write down the reasons why you feel you **ABSOLUTELY MUST** accomplish your objectives.

A)
B)
C)
D)

3) Please write down what you feel you **ABSOLUTELY MUST** do to accomplish your objectives.

A)
B)
C)
D)

4) Please write down all excuses that keep you from attaining your objectives.

A)
B)
C)
D)

5) Do you feel confident you can accomplish your objectives, and if not, what questions do you ask about them?

A)
B)
C)
D)

Empowering Questions

After you have established your objectives and how you communicate to yourself about them on the deepest level of the subconscious, you need to initiate control and implement your new programming. You will do this by turning your objectives, statements, and questions from The Subconscious Perspective into positive **Empowering Questions**. This begins the process of restructuring your subconscious.

What Determines Human Behavior?

What determines human behavior is simply **Information,** and the components of that information are words and pictures. You could not do anything without going through this process. In other words, **No Information = No Action**. The Subconscious Perspective and Empowering Questions address the first component of what brings about behavior, and this is your words.

How does your subconscious work?

Two key elements must exist to activate an emotional state, which in turn determines your behavior.

1) You must talk to yourself, which usually begins with a question

And

2) By asking yourself a question, your subconscious mind will always give you an answer, which in turn produces a correlating picture.

It is from this subconscious picture that your emotional state is determined, which, in turn, determines your behavior. If you have a means of intervening on these two key components, you can change how you feel, changing your behavior.

Example:

Keep in mind this is extremely slow motion. If I were to ask you where you went on vacation last, the subconscious process would go like this. You repeat the question to yourself, which evokes a picture of where you went on vacation. From this subconscious picture, you can tell me where you went on vacation and how you felt about the vacation. This is how the subconscious works and you would not be able to function or communicate without the subconscious going through this process.

This process looks like this, broken down into its most simplistic form.

Word - Picture - Emotion – Behavior

You must have the tools to intervene in this process if you want to have any control over your emotional state, behavior, and life. Philosophers have always stated in one way or another that life is all about your word. You will now fully understand why this is true.

Empowering Questions Defined

Before we get started on Empowering Questions, you need to understand why questions are the primary component for taking control of your subconscious programming. Now that you know you are asking yourself questions, the next question is, "Does your subconscious work on questions when you are not consciously involved?" Yes! If you have ever asked yourself, "What is that person's name?" You may not get an answer right away, but maybe in an hour or two or perhaps even the next day, while doing something completely unrelated, the answer pops into your head as clear as day.

Your subconscious will generate a response to absolutely every question you ask yourself, even if it has to make one up. False memories are created by someone continually asking you for an answer to a question the subconscious does not have stored. This can be a tremendous benefit if you are the one who has control over the questions. If you do not have control over your internal dialogue, especially your internal questions, anyone can use this process to take control of your subconscious.

When I ask you a question, what part of your consciousness usually gives you a response? You have to retrieve an answer from your subconscious. If I ask you a question about questions you ask yourself, you have now gained access to the deepest level of the subconscious. This is the very beginning of the process that brings about an emotional state, which in turn determines your behavior. This is why turning every response from the Subconscious Perspective into an Empowering Question is essential. This will immediately engage the subconscious and force it to move in your predetermined direction.

Now that you know the subconscious works on questions when you are not consciously involved, how important does the structure of the questions you ask yourself become? It becomes very important because if you are now asking yourself questions like. "Why can't I maintain a consistent exercise program?" or "Why can't I stop eating unhealthy foods?" or "Why can't I accomplish my objectives?" What do you think the results of these questions will be? They will give you more excuses or keep you anchored to what you do not want.

Most **empowering questions will begin with: "How can I?" or "What actions do I need to take**?" or "**What do I need to do to**?" For example, If one of your objectives is to lose 25 pounds and maintain a more consistent fitness program, an **Empowering Question** might be: "How can I permanently lose 25 pounds and have more fun with my fitness plan?" You do not have to agonize over a question. All you have to do is continue asking, and eventually, the subconscious will come up with an answer. You must ensure you continue returning and repeating your **Empowering Questions** until they are answered. Once all of your questions are answered, ask yourself…"Am I completely happy with this answer, or is this the answer that will work best for me?"

There are Empowering Question Samples of this Step if you need to refer to them. You will start the process of **Empowering Questions** with your objectives.

Empowering Questions and Answers

Turn all responses from the **Subconscious Perspective** into Empowering Questions.

Empowering Questions   **Answers**

My Objectives	My Objectives
A) Love:	**A)** Love:
B) Health:	**B)** Health:
C) Wealth:	**C)** Wealth:
D) Self-Image:	**D)** Self-Image:
Why I Absolutely Must Do It	**Why I Absolutely Must Do It**
A)	**A)**
B)	**B)**
C)	**C)**
D)	**D)**
What I Absolutely Must Do	**What I Absolutely Must Do**
A)	**A)**
B)	**B)**
C)	**C)**
D)	**D)**
Excuses for Not Doing it	**Excuses for Not Doing it**
A)	**A)**
B)	**B)**
C)	**C)**
D)	**D)**
Questions About My Objectives	**Questions About My Objectives**
A)	**A)**
B)	**B)**
C)	**C)**
D)	**D)**
Notes	**Notes**

Empowering Questions Samples

Following are samples of Empowering Questions for your Subconscious Perspective.

1) Please write one objective per category you ABSOLUTELY MUST accomplish.

Why do you set objectives? You establish objectives to give the mind someplace to go because if you do not determine where you want to go, the subconscious will decide for you. The two key words when establishing your objectives are **ABSOLUTELY MUST**. Following are samples of how to turn your objectives into Empowering Questions, which will engage the subconscious and begin the process of taking control of your programming.

If your objective was	Your empowering question might be
Love: Be more loving toward my family, friends, and me.	**Love:** How can I ensure love is always my life's dominant emotional state?
Health: Lose 20 pounds and improve my level of fitness.	**Health:** How must I change my eating behavior and improve my fitness level?
Wealth: Increase my income and manage my money better.	**Wealth:** What do I need to do to increase my income and manage my money better?
Self-Image: I would like to have a positive image of myself that makes me feel powerful.	**Self-Image:** What must I do to establish a more positive, empowering self-image in the subconscious?

2) Please write down the reasons why you feel you ABSOLUTELY MUST accomplish your objectives.

We refer to your reasons for accomplishing your objectives as anchors. Anchors are what attach you to any one particular behavior. First, you give the mind somewhere to go, and then you anchor yourself to those new objectives to ensure you will keep moving toward them.

Excuses are also anchors, but they keep you attached to what you do not want. In just one minute, I will show you how to use those excuses as a fast-moving vehicle that will move you toward your objective instead of keeping you away from it, which is what they are doing now. Following are samples of how to turn your reasons into Empowering Questions.

If your reason was	The empowering question might be
Love: Love is my most powerful emotional state and will positively affect every aspect of my life.	**Love:** What must I do to ensure I am always empowered to make everything in my life work for me?
Health: I will feel much better about myself and have more energy for everything I love to do.	**Health:** How can I feel better about myself every day while improving my energy level?
Wealth: I will feel less stress about money and be able to focus more on everything I love.	**Wealth:** What do I need to decrease my stress and continually maintain my most powerful emotional state?
Self-Image: A more positive self-image will attract the kind of people I want to be with..	**Self-Image:** How can I be more of a magnet to the people I want in my environment?

3) Please write down what you feel you ABSOLUTELY MUST do to accomplish your objectives.

Writing down what you must do to accomplish your objectives is like making a map. You must clearly define what action needs to be taken to get from point A to point B. It is also important because you can turn that map into **Empowering Questions**, which you will do now.

If what you absolutely must do was	The empowering question might be
Love: Restructure and replace all negative emotional states that keep me from my perfect love.	**Love:** What must I do to restructure and replace all negative emotional states with my most powerful emotional state?
Health: I need to stop wasting time on people, information, and emotional states that do not work.	**Health:** How can I process people and information more quickly so I have more time to focus on my health?
Wealth: I need to manage my time better so I can stay focused on my work and increase my income.	**Wealth:** How can I manage everything in my life better so I can focus more on what I need to do to increase my income?
Self-Image: I need to be more consistent with processing my old self-image and maintaining my new subconscious self-image.	**Self-Image:** How can I ensure I never allow my old self-image to reemerge into my subconscious?

4) Please write down all of the excuses that keep you from attaining your objectives.

If you turn your excuse into a positive, **Empowering Question** and continue to repeat it, the mind will no longer be able to use it as an excuse. For example, if one of your excuses is time, you can turn that excuse into a question such as…"How can I find more time to spend on my diet and exercise program and have a good time with it?"

What you have done is not only pull that anchor up, but it has also become a high-speed vehicle to move you more quickly toward your objectives. This is why you must write down every excuse you can think of because you can immediately turn it into a fast-moving vehicle instead of dead weight regarding your objectives. Following are samples of how to turn your excuses into Empowering Questions.

If your excuse was	The empowering question might be
Love: Stress from my job does not allow me to focus on myself or my family.	**Love:** How can I reduce my job stress so I can focus more loving time on myself and my family?
Health: I do not have the time to go to the gym.	**Health:** How can I find more time to spend on my food and fitness program and have fun with it?
Wealth: My job does not pay enough.	**Wealth:** What changes do I need to make in my work situation to make more money?
Self-Image: I am overweight, and I just do not feel good about myself.	**Self-Image:** What do I need to do to permanently destroy my negative self-image and permanently install a positive, empowering self-image in the subconscious?

5) Do you feel confident you can accomplish your objectives, and if not, what questions do you ask about them?

Why is this question THE key component regarding your subconscious? As stated earlier, the questions you ask yourself are the very beginning of an emotional state, which in turn equals a behavior. Responding to this question helps you understand how you communicate with yourself in relationship to your objectives on the deepest level of the subconscious.

If you have any questions written down in the Subconscious Perspective that have a don't or can't in them, these questions will be turned into **Empowering Questions** such as: "How can I keep myself on a consistent fitness program and have a good time doing it?" *or* "How can I make sure I only eat foods that work for me?" *or* "What action do I need to take to make sure I am always moving quickly toward my objectives?" If you are not happy with the results you are getting, this is one of the things you **ABSOLUTELY MUST** do consistently if you want to make a change.

You must listen to your self-talk and change every negative question you ask yourself into a positive, **Empowering Question**. Ask yourself if you will be completely happy with the results of your questions in question 5. If the answer is no, restructure every question in a form that will empower you and continue to repeat it until you get what you want.

If your question was	The empowering question might be
Love: Why don't I feel any love from my family or friends?	**Love:** How can I be more receptive to the love from my family and friends?
Health: Why can't I stop eating unhealthy foods and stay consistent with my fitness program?	**Health:** What do I need to restructure that drives me to make poor food choices, and how can I be more consistent with my fitness program?
Wealth: Why do I stay with a job that does not pay me enough?	**Wealth:** What changes do I need to make in my work situation to make more money?
Self-Image: Why do I feel so negative about myself?	**Self-Image:** What do I need to do consistently that will allow me to maintain a positive, empowering image of myself permanently?

There are five key questions you will be asking yourself every day:

1) Does this work for me?

2) How do I feel, and will I benefit from the results of this?

If the answer to this is no, ask yourself this next question.

3) What can I replace this with that I will benefit from?

The two key questions to use instead of reprimanding yourself are:

4) What can I learn from this? *and*

5) How can I use this experience to move myself more quickly toward my objectives?

There is a detailed explanation of the importance of these key questions in Step 5, The Heart of SR™.

SUBCONSCIOUS SELF-IMAGE

*There will never be a more critical image in your subconscious mind
or a more meaningful image you will need to change than the image you have
of yourself right now.*

This is Step 3 of the process, which addresses the second component of **Information** which determines your emotional state and in turn determines your behavior..."Your Subconscious Pictures"

There is a question you need to ask yourself before starting on this one, and that is. Do you feel good about yourself right now? Starting right now, you must feel fantastic about yourself on all levels. The subconscious has nowhere to go if you do not feel good about yourself right now.

Example: If you see yourself as out of shape, insecure with your job or relationship, have a low self-image, or are continuously subjected to a previous traumatic event and do not know how to restructure this information, the subconscious will do what it does best and continue to maintain this unwanted image.

If you set an objective that has to do with a change of your physical image without restructuring the image in your subconscious, your chances of success are, at best, remote. It is like wearing clothes that do not fit. You can wear them, but you are never comfortable. This discomfort will lead you back to where you began.

The best example of the importance of your subconscious self-imagery is people who cannot maintain consistent weight loss. One of the primary reasons for not maintaining their weight is that they did not restructure their image of themselves before they started. Once they achieve their objective weight, the subconscious does everything possible to get them back to the image that was locked in the subconscious.

As you now know, the image you have of yourself in your subconscious mind must match all of your objectives, not just body image. **Writing down a detailed description of your new self-image will be the most effective way of implanting your new self-image into your subconscious.** Going back and reading the description of your new self-image as part of your daily program will make this image a permanent part of your new subconscious programming.

Again, I will ask you questions to generate as clear a picture as possible. If you do not need the questions, go directly to the Subconscious Self-Image form..

Subconscious Self-Image

1) Please describe in detail how you look and feel emotionally, spiritually, and physically after attaining your objectives.

Questions for Your New Self-Image

- Do you see yourself as firm and toned?
- What is the weight of your new body?
- What are the measurements of your chest and waist?
- Do you feel a greater sense of spiritual strength?
- How are other people reacting to you in this picture?

You must learn to associate activities you will enjoy with your new self-image because becoming more active is essential in attaining and maintaining a positive self-image. With this in mind, let us continue.

2) Please describe the activities you see yourself participating in after attaining your objectives.

Questions for Your Activities

- Do you see yourself doing aerobics, jogging, lifting weights, walking briskly, or maybe just parking further away from the entrance while shopping?
- Do you feel like you have become more of a magnet for everything you desire?
- What location could you put yourself in that would give you the most incredible feeling? Example: On vacation with someone you love, with family and friends, or maybe in a quiet place just meditating.
- Do you feel a tremendous sense of accomplishment? Not just over yourself but the things around you as well?

The subconscious will always move toward pleasure and away from pain. This is why your new subconscious self-image must be detailed and crystal clear, and you derive tremendous pleasure from it.

Subconscious Self-Image

1) Please describe in detail how you look and feel emotionally, spiritually, and physically after attaining your objectives.

2) Please describe the activities you see yourself participating in after attaining your objectives.

Notes

Writer Producer Director

You are now the writer, producer, and director of your subconscious self-image. You can create the exact image you wish. You can participate in an activity you enjoy and in an emotional state and location that makes you feel incredible. Make your new subconscious body image as real and pleasurable as possible.

Maintenance Questions

What do you do if you struggle to maintain your new image? Questions play an important role here as well. If you are having difficulty maintaining the new perception of yourself, ask the following questions.

1) How can I maintain the image of this positive perception every second, every minute, every hour of the day?

2) What do I need to do to maintain this new image?

3) What can I add to the picture to help me maintain this new image?

4) What do I need to do to feel constantly fantastic?

5) What action do I need to take today that will make me feel great?

   Any time you run out of questions, ask yourself:

6) What questions can I ask myself that will help me maintain this new positive, empowering image?

There is one more variable here: there might be something in the way of consistently maintaining your new pictures. If so, ask yourself the next two questions:

7) What is getting in the way of maintaining my new picture? *Or*

8) What do I need to restructure that will help clear up the image of my new picture?

You need to go back and reread your three responses from your Subconscious Self-Image every day because you need to have a very clear vision of how the new self appears and, most importantly, emotionally, spiritually, and physically. Every time you reread this, you are restructuring the old programming. Restructuring is essential until the subconscious accepts this new picture of how you should look and feel.

The Structure of Your Subconscious Pictures

How you can determine positive from negative experiences is the way an image is stored in the subconscious or the structure of that image. Following, you will discover how you store the visual information that creates a positive emotional state for you and then use that information to help you maintain your focus and motivation toward your objectives.

I think we can all agree we are all basically wired the same, but the reason one person loses motivation and another says never quit lies in how we code our internal pictures. In other words, every person's perception of what they are doing differs. This is why two people can experience the same event but have different perceptions or feelings about it.

Before we begin, you need to understand how to Associate and Dissociate. Right now, association and dissociation happen automatically; in other words, how you feel about events in your life will determine whether you associate or dissociate with the experience. If you are out of shape, over or under-eat, or are abusive toward your body, you are dissociating from it. Association and dissociation must be intentional if you want greater control over how you feel. Association and dissociation are the equivalent of you watching your life's movie. If I ask you to **Dissociate** from a picture, that means you are in the theatre looking at yourself in the picture.

You may need to further dissociate from the picture if it is one that you are particularly uncomfortable with. This means you will put yourself in the balcony looking down at yourself, watching yourself in the picture. When I ask you to **Associate** with a picture of yourself, this means you place yourself in the picture and fully become part of that experience.

You will now begin with defining the structure of a subconscious picture. Make sure you are in a quiet place where you can fully concentrate. Think about your new self-image as you detailed it in the Subconscious Self-Image and establish all the positive associated feelings of love, health, and wealth. Do whatever you need to focus and concentrate fully on the formation of this picture. Looking at this picture, you feel total love and feel life could not be better. It could be a vacation, a new love, or whatever you wish. You will refer to this picture as your **Motivation Picture**.

Once you have established your new image, we will explore the composition. Is the picture you see of this experience in color or black and white? If it is in black and white, turn it into color; if it is already in color, make the colors more pleasing and vibrant. Is the picture framed, unframed, or panoramic? If the picture is framed or a certain size, make it panoramic so it completely encompasses your field of vision. Is the picture moving like a film, or is it still? If the picture is still, add movement. If the picture is too fast or too slow, adjust the speed so it is completely comfortable for you. Is there sound in the form of voices, music, ambient, or nothing? If you find a voice or voices immensely pleasing, add them and delete the rest; now, add your favorite music or ambient sounds like ocean waves, birds chirping, or a gentle breeze.

Is the picture bright and clear or slightly out of focus? If the picture is out of focus, make it perfectly clear; if it is clear, make it brighter, sharper, and clearer until it is overwhelmingly pleasing. Please take a few moments to structure this picture so it is the most compelling experience you have ever had. Now, associate with this picture and place yourself in that experience. Give yourself a moment to solidly plant yourself in the picture. Did you feel different when you became part of this experience? Step out of this picture and put the image aside for a moment, and we will establish what you will refer to as your **Objective Picture**.

This time, please create a picture of yourself moving toward one or more of the objectives you established in the Subconscious Perspective. Take a moment and be sure to get a clear image of this picture. When you have established the image, let us look at the composition. Is the picture in color or black and white? Is the picture framed, unframed, or panoramic? How big is the image, and where is it located? Is the picture moving like a film, or is it still? Is the speed fast, slow, or normal if it is moving? Is there sound in the form of voices, ambient, or nothing? Is the picture bright and clear or slightly out of focus?

Once you have established the composition of the **Objective Picture,** please bring back the motivation picture and place it in front of the **Objective Picture**. Step into the motivation picture and completely associate with it. Now, punch a tiny pinhole through the motivation picture so you can look through it and see the **Objective Picture**.

While looking through the pinhole, change the Objective Picture's stru**cture** to match the motivation picture. In other words, turn the Objective Picture into color if it is in black and white. Now, make it panoramic. Do the same with the sound, speed, resolution, and any other differences you can see. Once you have reframed your **Objective Picture,** change the image of yourself until you see exactly what you want. Pause for a moment to ensure that your mind, body, and spirit in this picture are precisely what you want. Be sure to establish the exact physical dimensions you want and the purest feelings of love for the person in that picture. Be sure you remain in the motivation picture while occasionally looking through the pinhole, seeing yourself in control, and doing what you feel is necessary to accomplish your objectives.

If you have trouble restructuring the **Objective Picture** to match the motivation picture, you can fuse the **Objective Picture** with the motivation picture. In other words, move the **Objective Picture** into the motivation picture until both pictures become one, and you see yourself in the motivation picture going through your daily fitness plan. This technique can be used with any objective that needs more motivation.

STEP 4

THE STOP & REPLACE SYSTEM

This is the most powerful part of the Subconscious Restructuring™ process. The Stop and Replace System will enable you to interrupt any subconscious programming you wish to change and dramatically change your emotional state and behavior. This is accomplished by using the same process that created the program. All the elements from the first three Steps of the program are used on this page to help you **Interrupt, Restructure,** and **Reprogram** any subconscious information that does not work for you.

Here is a brief reminder of how the subconscious works:

Two key elements must exist to activate an emotional state, which determines your behavior.

1) You must talk to yourself, which usually begins with a question

And

2) By asking yourself a question, your subconscious mind will always give you an answer, which in turn produces a correlating picture.

It is from this subconscious picture that your emotional state is determined and, in turn, determines your behavior. If you have a means of interrupting and restructuring these two key components, you can reprogram the way you feel, changing your behavior.

This process, broken down into its most simplistic form, looks like this.

Word - Picture - Emotion - Behavior

We will begin with the three emotional states that have the potential to cause the most damage: Fear (Anxiety), Guilt (negative self-talk), and Anger unless you decide on something else. We start the program with these three emotions because fear and guilt are used on all of us as children to try to control our behavior, and at some point, fear and guilt turn into anger.

The STOP and REPLACE System Breakdown

Please look at the Stop and Replace breakdown on the following page. Each step will be in bold, followed by an explanation. There are seven components to the Stop and Replace System, with three parts to The Switch Pattern, which is the seventh step.

STOP & REPLACE System Breakdown

Please write down one habit, behavior, or emotional state you

absolutely must interrupt, restructure, and reprogram in the box below.

➤ You will write down what you wish to restructure here.

Benefits of NOT doing this	Empowering Questions
1) This is where you will write down your benefits.	**1)** This is where you turn your benefit into an empowering question.
2)	**2)**
3)	**3)**
4)	**4)**

Answers to Empowering Questions:

1) This is where you write your answers to your empowering questions.
2)
3)
4)

Describe your Replacement Picture: ➤ **Associated**

This is where you will describe your new picture.

Describe your Old Picture: ➤ **Dissociated**

This is where you will describe your old picture.

The Switch Pattern

1) CUE: When you recognize your cue, you will say **STOP** to yourself.
2) STOP: Your old picture will be destroyed when you say STOP.

➤ **SWITCH PATTERN**

3) REPLACE: When you say the word **REPLACE,** your subconscious mind will produce your new active body image.

Stop and Replace System Samples

Following are ten Stop and Replace System samples. If you look at the first one, you will notice the **Benefits of NOT doing this,** and **Empowering Questions** are filled out for you. These samples are meant to help you get started with the Stop and Replace System. You should use information from the samples only if it specifically applies to you. If you want to skip over the samples and get started, go directly to the blank forms.

The STOP & REPLACE System Samples

Please write down one habit, behavior, or emotional state you absolutely must interrupt, restructure, and reprogram in the box below.

> **Fear (Anxiety)**

Benefits of NOT doing this	**Empowering Questions**
1) I will not procrastinate over things I know what needs to be done.	**1)** How can I restructure procrastination?
2) I will feel a greater sense of control over everything I do.	**2)** How can I gain a greater sense of control over everything I do?
3) My decision-making power will improve significantly.	**3)** How can I increase my decision making power?
4) I will be able to move more quickly toward my objectives.	**4)** How can I move more quickly toward my objectives?

Answers to Empowering Questions:

1)

2)

3)

4)

Describe your Replacement Picture: ➢ **Associated**

Describe your Old Picture: ➢ **Dissociated**

The Switch Pattern

1) CUE:

2) STOP:

      ➢ **SWITCH PATTERN**

3) REPLACE:

The STOP & REPLACE System Samples

Please write down one habit, behavior, or emotional state you

absolutely must interrupt, restructure, and reprogram in the box below.

> **Guilt**

Benefits of NOT doing this	Empowering Questions
1) I will be able to eliminate my negative self-talk.	**1)** How can I eliminate my negative self-talk?
2) I will feel better emotionally.	**2)** What do I need to do to feel better all the time?
3) I will eliminate behaviors that make me feel guilty.	**3)** How can I eliminate behaviors that make me feel guilty?
4) I will be able to eliminate guilt as an excuse for over (under) eating.	**4)** How can I eliminate guilt as an excuse for over (under) eating?

Answers to Empowering Questions:

1)

2)

3)

4)

Describe your Replacement Picture: > **Associated**

Describe your Old Picture: > **Dissociated**

The Switch Pattern

1) CUE:

2) STOP:

                              > **SWITCH PATTERN**

3) REPLACE:

The STOP & REPLACE System Samples

Please write down one habit, behavior, or emotional state you

absolutely must interrupt, restructure, and reprogram in the box below.

➢ **Anger**

Benefits of NOT doing this	Empowering Questions
1) I will have complete control over my communication skills.	**1)** How can I improve my communication skills?
2) I will not be able to use anger as an excuse to over (under) eat.	**2)** How can I eliminate anger as an excuse to over (under) eat?
3) I will be more loving toward myself family and friends.	**3)** How can I be more loving toward myself, family, and friends?
4) I will have more fun with life.	**4)** How can I have more fun with everything I do in life?

Answers to Empowering Questions:

1)
2)
3)
4)

Describe your Replacement Picture: ➢ **Associated**

Describe your Old Picture: ➢ **Dissociated**

The Switch Pattern

1) CUE:

2) STOP:
➢ **SWITCH PATTERN**

3) REPLACE:

The STOP & REPLACE System Samples

Please write down one habit, behavior, or emotional state you

absolutely must interrupt, restructure, and reprogram in the box below.

> **Negative Self Talk**

Benefits of NOT doing this	Empowering Questions
1) My self-esteem will significantly improve.	**1)** What do I need to do to upgrade my self-esteem?
2) I will feel better about everything I do in life.	**2)** How can I feel better about everything **I do in life?**
3) I will feel more confident in every aspect of my life.	**3)** How can I increase my confidence?
4) I will be able to move more quickly toward my objectives.	**4)** How can I move more quickly toward my objectives?

Answers to Empowering Questions:

1)
2)
3)
4)

Describe your Replacement Picture: > **Associated**

Describe your Old Picture: > **Dissociated**

The Switch Pattern

1) CUE:

2) STOP:

> **SWITCH PATTERN**

3) REPLACE:

The STOP & REPLACE System Samples

Please write down one habit, behavior, or emotional state you absolutely must interrupt, restructure, and reprogram in the box below.

> **Procrastination**

Benefits of NOT doing this	Empowering Questions
1) I will feel more in control over every aspect of my life.	**1)** How can I gain more control over every aspect of my life?
2) I will be able to establish and maintain greater self-esteem.	**2)** How can I establish and maintain a greater self-esteem?
3) I will have a more loving relationship with family, friends, and myself.	**3)** What do I need to do to be more loving toward family, friends & myself?
4) I will feel more comfortable in social situations.	**4)** How can I feel more comfortable in social situations?

Answers to Empowering Questions:

1)

2)

3)

4)

Describe your Replacement Picture: > **Associated**

Describe your Old Picture: > **Dissociated**

The Switch Pattern

1) CUE:

2) STOP:

> **SWITCH PATTERN**

3) REPLACE:

The STOP & REPLACE System Samples

Please write down one habit, behavior, or emotional state you absolutely must interrupt, restructure, and reprogram in the box below.

➤ Drugs & Alcohol	
Benefits of NOT doing this	**Empowering Questions**
1) I will not predispose myself to liver, heart disease and high blood pressure.	**1)** What can I do every day to improve my overall health?
2) I will not damage my brain, and I will improve my decision-making power.	**2)** What do I need to do to assure optimum brain–mind health?
3) I will always be able to drive myself home.	**3)** How can I make sure I never have to leave my car anywhere?
4) I will have a greater level of power over myself and the things around me.	**4)** What action do I need to take to increase my self-power and control?

Answers to Empowering Questions:

1)
2)
3)
4)

Describe your Replacement Picture: ➤ **Associated**

Describe your Old Picture: ➤ **Dissociated**

The Switch Pattern

1) CUE:
2) STOP:
➤ **SWITCH PATTERN**
3) REPLACE:

The STOP & REPLACE System Samples

Please write down one habit, behavior, or emotional state you

absolutely must interrupt, restructure, and reprogram in the box below.

➢ Over (Under) Eating

Benefits of NOT doing this	Empowering Questions
1) I will feel more in control over every aspect of my life.	**1)** How can I gain more control over every aspect of my life?
2) I will be able to establish and maintain greater self-esteem.	**2)** How can I establish and maintain a greater self-esteem?
3) I will have a more loving relationship with myself, family, and friends.	**3)** What do I need to do to be more loving toward family, friends & myself?
4) I will feel more comfortable in social situations.	**4)** How can I feel more comfortable in social situations?

Answers to Empowering Questions:

1)
2)
3)
4)

Describe your Replacement Picture: ➢ **Associated**

Describe your Old Picture: ➢ **Dissociated**

The Switch Pattern

1) CUE:

2) STOP:
➢ **SWITCH PATTERN**

3) REPLACE:

The STOP & REPLACE System Samples

Please write down one habit, behavior, or emotional state you

absolutely must interrupt, restructure, and reprogram in the box below.

➤ Smoking

Benefits of NOT doing this	Empowering Questions
1) I will not predispose myself to lung cancer and heart disease.	**1)** How can I improve the health of my heart and lungs?
2) My breath, home, and clothes will not smell like stale smoke.	**2)** How can I improve the fragrance of my breath, home, and clothes?
3) I will not have yellow/brown tobacco stained teeth.	**3)** What do I need to do to brighten my smile?
4) I will not continually offend people who do not smoke.	**4)** How can I improve my rapport skills?

Answers to Empowering Questions:

1)
2)
3)
4)

Describe your Replacement Picture: ➤ **Associated**

Describe your Old Picture: ➤ **Dissociated**

The Switch Pattern

1) CUE:

2) STOP:
➤ **SWITCH PATTERN**

3) REPLACE:

The STOP & REPLACE System Samples

Please write down one habit, behavior, or emotional state you

absolutely must interrupt, restructure, and reprogram in the box below.

➢ Coffee	
Benefits of NOT doing this	**Empowering Questions**
1) I will not have brown teeth and bad breath.	**1)** What do I need to do to improve the appearance of my mouth?
2) I will increase my insulin sensitivity by 15%.	**2)** How can I increase my insulin sensitivity?
3) I will not increase my homocysteine to dangerous levels.	**3)** How can I better manage my homocysteine level?
4) I will have more patience for people I care about.	**4)** How can I be more patient with the people I care about?

Answers to Empowering Questions:

1)
2)
3)
4)

Describe your Replacement Picture: ➢ **Associated**

Describe your Old Picture: ➢ **Dissociated**

The Switch Pattern

1) CUE:
2) STOP:
➢ **SWITCH PATTERN**
3) REPLACE:

The STOP & REPLACE System Samples

Please write down one habit, behavior, or emotional state you

absolutely must interrupt, restructure, and reprogram in the box below.

> **Sugar**

Benefits of NOT doing this	Empowering Questions
1) I will not be eating empty calories that add fat instead of muscle.	**1)** How can I eliminate empty calories?
2) I will not be doing constant damage to my teeth and gums.	**2)** What do I need to do to eliminate damage to my teeth and gums?
3) I will not have to suffer through the low points and mood swings.	**3)** How can I eliminate my emotional low points and mood swings?
4) I will have more energy for the things I enjoy.	**4)** How can I find more energy for the things I enjoy?

Answers to Empowering Questions:

1)

2)

3)

4)

Describe your Replacement Picture: > **Associated**

Describe your Old Picture: > **Dissociated**

The Switch Pattern

1) CUE:

2) STOP:

      > **SWITCH PATTERN**

3) REPLACE:

The Stop and Replace System Overview

Following are the blank Stop and Replace System Sheets. You will use these sheets to restructure programming that does not work for you. How often and how long will you need to restructure an old program has several variables, and they are:

1) Age

2) Gender

3) How much physical abuse or trauma was used to reinforce your programming?

The bottom line is that this is the most powerful tool for taking control of your subconscious programming. You must decide to what extent you wish to change and how much restructuring you wish to do on your old programming.

Fear, Guilt, and Anger

Fear and guilt are used on us as children to try to control our behavior. As a result, these two emotional states eventually turn into anger. This is why we start by guiding you through the process of restructuring these emotional states because they are also the most limiting. What you wish to restructure from there is up to you. Fear, guilt, and anger are the motivations behind a wide spectrum of behaviors that do not work. Some people think they have to have fear, so they do not do things like jump off a tall building. You do not have to be afraid of heights to keep yourself from jumping off a tall building. All you need to know is what the results will be, and that is usually enough. Does the emotional state of fear ever need to be more than concern? The quick answer is no. You will ultimately decide when you are comfortable with this emotional state.

If any emotional state is debilitating to you in any way, you need to immediately interrupt, restructure, and reprogram it until you control it, and it does not control you.

Fear

You will begin the process of restructuring with fear. Please write Fear in the box with the arrow at the top of the first blank Stop and Replace System below. If there is something specific to you, such as fear of crowds, etc., write that next to it. Fear can also include doubt, insecurity, etc. In other words, you could be insecure about accomplishing your objectives, how you look, and your relationships. All of these pertain to Fear.

Benefits of NOT doing this and Empowering Questions

In the left column below fear, it states Benefits of NOT doing this. If you have difficulty thinking of the Benefits of not being fearful, refer to the Stop and Replace Samples. If you refer to the samples, only use the information there if it is specific to you. Remember you also refer to the Benefits of doing something as anchors, so you are moving away from what you wish to restructure. What might the advantages be for not being fearful? Can fear keep you from getting things done? Yes. If this applies, write in. "I will not procrastinate over things I know need to be done." In the right-hand column, you will write a correlating **Empowering Question**. If your positive anchor was "I will not procrastinate," the **Empowering Question** would be…"How can I restructure procrastination?"

You have now begun moving away from fear by realizing the Benefit of not being fearful and asking a question that will begin to move you toward something that will empower you. Something else has also happened here. You have also uncovered something else you want to restructure, which is, of course, procrastination. When writing down Benefits of NOT doing this, you will often uncover other things you may want to restructure, so **always scrutinize your Benefits for anything else you wish to restructure.**

What other positive benefits might there be for not being fearful? If you do not procrastinate, you will be more productive, so your next benefit might be…"I will be more productive." The **Empowering Question** would then be…"How can I increase my productivity?" If you are not spending time on fear or procrastinating, then you will have a lot more time to spend on your food and fitness plan and other things you enjoy; so the next benefit of not being fearful might be: "I will have more time to spend on my food and fitness plan and other things I enjoy." The **Empowering Question** would be…"How can I find more time to spend on my food, fitness plan, and other things I enjoy?" Would the elimination of fear give you more control? Yes! Therefore, the last benefit of not being fearful might be…"I will have greater control over my environment and myself." The **Empowering Question** would be…"How can I gain greater control over my environment and myself?"

Answers to Empowering Questions

Below the Benefits and **Empowering Questions,** you will see a space for Answers to **Empowering Questions**. Be sure to fill this in when the answers come to you. Remember, you do not have to sit and work on a question. Just keep asking, and the subconscious will eventually give you one. It is essential to return to this every day and continue asking these questions until you are completely happy with the answers.

Describe your Replacement Picture - Associated

Describe your Replacement Picture. The most important question to ask yourself when restructuring a behavior is. What can I use to replace this habit, behavior, or emotional state with that will benefit me?

You cannot just quit something and leave a blank spot in your mind; you must replace it with something before you quit. A good example of this is someone who says…"I can't quit smoking. I'll gain weight." You gain weight because you did not make a conscious choice of what you were going to replace the habit with, so your subconscious mind chose for you.

There are no limits for this replacement picture. You do, however, want to make the replacement picture as compelling as possible, which means you want to focus on the results as opposed to the process. In other words, everyone likes the results of exercise, but very few people enjoy the process, so creating an image that is the most compelling to you is important. The basis for this new picture must be a combination of the results of the objectives you listed in Step 2 in the Subconscious Perspective and the description of the new self you wrote down in Step 3, the Subconscious Self-Image. After establishing the picture of the new self, enhance it in any way you can. For instance, add music if you have a favorite song, add whatever colors you want, or put people in the picture who make you feel good. Also, make sure you always focus on the results of your replacement picture.

Example: If fear is preventing you from getting something done, you want to establish a picture of having the task done as opposed to going through the process.

Describe your Old Picture - Dissociated

Now, write down a description of the old picture and remember to stay dissociated from this picture. Do you remember how to dissociate from your negative pictures? If not, go back to Step 3 and review.

"The Structure of Your Subconscious Pictures." **You must remain dissociated from all pictures you wish to change in your subconscious.**

Your Cue for Fear

After you have written down what the old picture looks like, I want you to look at it and then back it up. That's right! Go in reverse until right before you begin the behavior. This is known as your Cue. Your Cue is also referred to as a trigger. The Cue is the most difficult part of the Stop and Replace System, so if you cannot think of your Cue right now, do not concern yourself with it; just ask yourself: What is the Cue or trigger for this issue? It is important to recognize the Cue, so as soon as you think of it, write it down. There is always a beginning to every subconscious process, and you must stop it before it gains power and takes over what you truly want.

The Switch Pattern for Fear

Now for the fun part. Are you ready? We are going to learn how to do the switch pattern. First, I want you to get a clear vision of your Replacement Picture, **Associated**. Do you have a clear vision of your new picture? Once you have established that picture, set it aside for a moment. Now bring up your Old Picture, **Dissociated**. Remember, any time we talk about the old picture, make sure you remain dissociated from it by putting yourself in the back row of a theatre instead of being part of the picture.

When you recognize your Cue in the old picture, say **STOP** to yourself and then move the picture closer to you, making it smaller, smaller, darker, and darker until it's a little black BB right in front of your face.

Now shoot it back behind you and blow it up into a million molecules while saying **REPLACE** to yourself, which will simultaneously bring up the new picture. That is the Switch Pattern. This is how you restructure a behavior that does not work for you and create a positive, permanent change in the subconscious.

All the elements that constitute an emotional state and behavior are within the Stop and Replace System. As long as you assert control and consistently restructure the old process, you will have optimum control of your subconscious programming.

The STOP & REPLACE System: Fear (Anxiety)

Please write down one habit, behavior, or emotional state you

absolutely must interrupt, restructure, and reprogram in the box below.

➢

Benefits of NOT doing this	Empowering Questions
1)	1)
2)	2)
3)	3)
4)	4)

Answers to Empowering Questions:

1)
2)
3)
4)

Describe your Replacement Picture: ➢ **Associated**

Describe your Old Picture: ➢ **Dissociated**

The Switch Pattern

1) CUE:
2) STOP:

➢ **SWITCH PATTERN**

3) REPLACE:

Guilt

At the top of the next Stop and Replace System page, write in Guilt. If there is something specific to you, such as guilt from overting, not exercising, procrastination, etc., note that next to it.

Benefits of NOT doing this and Empowering Questions

In the left column below guilt, it states Benefits of NOT doing this. What might the benefits be for not being guilty? If you have difficulty thinking of the advantages of not being guilty, refer to The Stop and Replace samples. Remember, when you refer to a sample, only use the information there if it is specific to you.

What might be a big advantage for restructuring guilt? What does guilt do to you? Guilt tends to help generate negative self-talk. Restructuring guilt will help you eliminate your negative self-talk. The benefit or anchor then for not being guilty would be..."I will be able to eliminate my negative self-talk." If this is relative to you, write it down. An **Empowering Question** for this benefit might be..."What do I need to do to permanently eliminate my negative self-talk?"

Once again, you have uncovered something you want to restructure if you marked eliminating negative self-talk as one of your benefits or anchors. What other benefits or anchors are there for not being guilty? If you restructure guilt, will you feel better emotionally? Yes. Therefore, another benefit of not being guilty is..."I will feel better emotionally." A suggestion for the correlating **Empowering Question** would be..."What action must I take to improve my emotional state every day?"

Another benefit of not feeling guilt is..."I will eliminate behaviors that make me feel guilty." The **Empowering Question** would be..."How can I permanently Stop behaviors that make me feel guilty." Another benefit for not being guilty is..."I will be able to eliminate guilt as an excuse for overeating, not exercising, etc." The **Empowering Question** would be..."How can I permanently eliminate guilt as an excuse for over or under-eating and skipping my fitness plan?"

Answers to Empowering Questions

Be sure to fill in your Answers to **Empowering Questions** when the answers come to you. Drop down to your replacement picture.

Describe your Replacement Picture - Associated

Once again, the basis for this new picture needs to be a combination of the results of the objectives you listed in the Subconscious Perspective and the description of the new self you wrote down in the Subconscious Self-Image. After establishing the picture of the new self, make sure the structure is the same as your initial replacement picture and enhance it in any way you possibly can. For instance, add music to it if you have a favorite song, add whatever colors you want, or put people in the picture who make you feel good. Make sure you focus on the results of your replacement picture. Always go for the results of not feeling guilty and **Associate this picture with it**.

Describe your Old Picture - Dissociated

Make sure you keep yourself out in the theater audience when viewing this picture or up in the balcony looking down at yourself, looking at this picture.

Your Cue for Guilt

When you are done describing the old picture, continue to look at it and then run it backward until right before you begin the behavior. This is your cue.

The Switch Pattern for Guilt

Are you ready for the switch pattern? First, get a clear vision of the new picture and ensure you are a part of it. Once you have established that picture, please move it aside for a moment.

Now, establish a dissociated vision of the old picture. When you recognize the cue in the old picture, say **STOP** to yourself and then move the picture closer to you, making it smaller, smaller, darker, and darker until it's a little black BB right in front of your face. Now shoot it back behind you and blow it up into a million molecules while saying **REPLACE,** which simultaneously brings up the new picture.

The STOP & REPLACE System: Guilt

Please write down one habit, behavior, or emotional state you

absolutely must interrupt, restructure, and reprogram in the box below.

>

Benefits of NOT doing this	Empowering Questions
1)	1)
2)	2)
3)	3)
4)	4)

Answers to Empowering Questions:

1)
2)
3)
4)

Describe your Replacement Picture: ➢ **Associated**

Describe your Old Picture: ➢ **Dissociated**

The Switch Pattern

1) CUE:
2) STOP:
➢ **SWITCH PATTERN**
3) REPLACE:

The STOP & REPLACE System: Anger

Anger

Please write in anger in the box at the top of the next Stop and Replace System sheet. If there is something specific, add that to it. In other words, if you are angry toward yourself, a family member, a friend, your boss, or how your life is going.

Before we begin with anger, I have a question. What is missing when you are in a state of fear, guilt, or anger? When you are in a state of fear, guilt, or anger, do you communicate well, make good decisions, draw people into your environment that empower you, move quickly toward your objectives, or feel spiritually centered? No. What is missing when you are in a state of fear, guilt, or anger is your most empowered emotional state, which is love.

To be perfectly clear about this, we are not talking about being in love. We are speaking specifically about the emotional state of love.

The foundational purpose of SR™ is to interrupt and restructure any autonomic subconscious process, which may bring about an emotional state that does not work. In other words, life is not about external events but about how the subconscious processes those events.

Benefits of NOT doing this and Empowering Questions

What is one of the biggest Benefits of not being angry? What is usually significantly impaired when you get angry? Do you begin to communicate differently? Yes. Your first benefit for not being angry might be…"I will not lose control of my ability to communicate effectively." And, of course, the **Empowering Question** would be: "How can I improve my communication skills?"

What other benefits might there be for not being angry? Do you ever stuff this emotion with food? If the answer is yes, your next benefit for not doing this might be…"I will not be able to use anger as an excuse to over or under-eat." The **Empowering Question** would be…"How can I eliminate anger as an excuse to over or under-eat?"

Would you be more loving toward yourself, your family, and others? Yes. If this pertains to you, please write it down. The **Empowering Question** for this benefit would be…"How can I be more loving toward my family, others, and myself?"

Would you have more fun with life? Definitely! If this pertains to you, another benefit might be…"I will have more fun with life." The **Empowering Question** would be…"How can I have more fun with everything I do in life?"

Answers to Empowering Questions

Be sure to fill in your Answers to **Empowering Questions** when the answers come to you.

Describe your Replacement Picture - Associated

When you have finished the positive anchors and **Empowering Questions,** drop down and describe your new picture associated. Once again, the basis for your new picture needs to be a combination of the results of the objectives you listed in Step 2 of the Subconscious Perspective and the description of the new self you wrote down in Step 3 of the Subconscious Self-Image.

After establishing the picture of the new self, make sure the structure is the same as your initial replacement picture and enhance it in any way you can. For instance, add music to it if you have a favorite song, add whatever colors you want, or put people in the picture who make you feel good. Also, make sure you always focus on the results of whatever your replacement picture is.

Describe your Old Picture - Dissociated

When you have finished describing the new picture, describe the old picture, dissociated.

Your Cue for Anger

Were you able to recognize your cue? If you cannot clearly identify your cue, just ask yourself: What is the cue for this picture?

The Switch Pattern for Anger

Get a clear vision of the new picture and ensure you are a part of it. Once you have established that picture, move it aside for a moment. Now, establish a dissociated vision of the old picture. When you recognize your cue in the old picture, say **STOP** to yourself and then move the picture closer to you; make it smaller, smaller, darker, and darker until it's a little black BB right in front of your face. Now shoot it back behind you and blow it up into a million molecules while saying **REPLACE** to yourself, which simultaneously brings up the new picture.

The STOP & REPLACE System: Anger

Please write down one habit, behavior, or emotional state you

absolutely must interrupt, restructure, and reprogram in the box below.

➢

Benefits of NOT doing this	Empowering Questions
1)	1)
2)	2)
3)	3)
4)	4)

Answers to Empowering Questions:

1)
2)
3)
4)

Describe your Replacement Picture: ➢ **Associated**

Describe your Old Picture: ➢ **Dissociated**

The Switch Pattern

1) CUE:

2) STOP:

        ➢ **SWITCH PATTERN**

3) REPLACE:

Continue to Interrupt, Reprogram and Restructure

It is important to reread these sheets every day until you have completely destroyed the old program and installed a new one of your choice. If you have not begun to see significant results after 7 days, you will need to use another blank Stop and Replace sheet and rewrite all of your benefits, **Empowering Questions**, new and old pictures, and a clear identification of your Cue.

Whenever you reread your Stop and Replace sheet, you move closer to permanently restructuring an old subconscious program. This is how you learn what does not work and how you restructure it.

You have seven more blank Stop and Replace pages to take control of whatever may be controlling you that does not work. It is now up to you to determine what you are happy with and what you are not happy with.

The STOP & REPLACE System

Please write down one habit, behavior, or emotional state you

absolutely must interrupt, restructure, and reprogram in the box below.

> ➤

Benefits of NOT doing this	Empowering Questions
1)	1)
2)	2)
3)	3)
4)	4)

Answers to Empowering Questions:

1)
2)
3)
4)

Describe your Replacement Picture: ➤ **Associated**

Describe your Old Picture: ➤ **Dissociated**

The Switch Pattern

1) CUE:
2) STOP:
➤ **SWITCH PATTERN**
3) REPLACE:

The STOP & REPLACE System

Please write down one habit, behavior, or emotional state you

absolutely must interrupt, restructure, and reprogram in the box below.

> ➤

Benefits of NOT doing this	Empowering Questions
1)	1)
2)	2)
3)	3)
4)	4)

Answers to Empowering Questions:

1)
2)
3)
4)

Describe your Replacement Picture: ➤ **Associated**

Describe your Old Picture: ➤ **Dissociated**

The Switch Pattern

1) CUE:
2) STOP:
➤ **SWITCH PATTERN**
3) REPLACE:

The STOP & REPLACE System

Please write down one habit, behavior, or emotional state you

absolutely must interrupt, restructure, and reprogram in the box below.

➢

Benefits of NOT doing this	**Empowering Questions**
1)	1)
2)	2)
3)	3)
4)	4)

Answers to Empowering Questions:

1)
2)
3)
4)

Describe your Replacement Picture: ➢ **Associated**

Describe your Old Picture: ➢ **Dissociated**

The Switch Pattern

1) CUE:
2) STOP:

➢ **SWITCH PATTERN**

3) REPLACE:

The STOP & REPLACE System

Please write down one habit, behavior, or emotional state you

absolutely must interrupt, restructure, and reprogram in the box below.

> ➢

Benefits of NOT doing this	Empowering Questions
1)	1)
2)	2)
3)	3)
4)	4)

Answers to Empowering Questions:

1)
2)
3)
4)

Describe your Replacement Picture: ➢ **Associated**

Describe your Old Picture: ➢ **Dissociated**

The Switch Pattern

1) CUE:

2) STOP:

➢ **SWITCH PATTERN**

3) REPLACE:

The STOP & REPLACE System

Please write down one habit, behavior, or emotional state you

absolutely must interrupt, restructure, and reprogram in the box below.

> ➢

Benefits of NOT doing this	Empowering Questions
1)	1)
2)	2)
3)	3)
4)	4)

Answers to Empowering Questions:

1)
2)
3)
4)

Describe your Replacement Picture: ➢ **Associated**

Describe your Old Picture: ➢ **Dissociated**

The Switch Pattern

1) CUE:
2) STOP:
➢ **SWITCH PATTERN**
3) REPLACE:

The STOP & REPLACE System

Please write down one habit, behavior, or emotional state you

absolutely must interrupt, restructure, and reprogram in the box below.

> _____

Benefits of NOT doing this	Empowering Questions
1)	1)
2)	2)
3)	3)
4)	4)

Answers to Empowering Questions:

1)
2)
3)
4)

Describe your Replacement Picture: ➤ **Associated**

Describe your Old Picture: ➤ **Dissociated**

The Switch Pattern

1) CUE:
2) STOP:
➤ **SWITCH PATTERN**
3) REPLACE:

The STOP & REPLACE System

Please write down one habit, behavior, or emotional state you

absolutely must interrupt, restructure, and reprogram in the box below.

➢

Benefits of NOT doing this	Empowering Questions
1)	1)
2)	2)
3)	3)
4)	4)

Answers to Empowering Questions:

1)
2)
3)
4)

Describe your Replacement Picture: ➢ **Associated**

Describe your Old Picture: ➢ **Dissociated**

The Switch Pattern

1) CUE:
2) STOP:
➢ **SWITCH PATTERN**
3) REPLACE:

Dramatic Results

The most dramatic results you will ever achieve for something you wish to change will be made using the Stop and Replace System. The Stop and Replace System will allow you to take control anytime you choose. You are no longer subject to what you have learned or how you have been programmed. You can now ultimately decide what information remains in the subconscious and what information will not. The only question regarding using the Stop and Replace system regularly is..."Do I want random programming to control me, or do I want to take control of my programming?"

STEP 5

THE HEART OF SR™

Your Pathway to Positive Empowering Change

The Heart of SR™ consists of your **Love, Health, Wealth, and Self Image.** Now that you understand how to take control of your emotional state and behavior, you must use these skills daily. How you process information can be dramatically changed quickly by consistently implementing The Heart of SR™.

Feel free to bend, shape, rearrange, and change any questions to suit your exact needs. **It is imperative you ask yourself a minimum of one question per category every night before you go to bed and every morning after you get up.** This is the least you must do to maintain control of your subconscious.

The Five Key Questions

The First Three Key Questions You Will Ask Yourself About Everything Through the Course of Your Day Are:

1) Does this work for me?

2) How do I feel, and will I benefit from the **results** of this? (If the answer is no, ask yourself this next question)

3) What can I replace this with that I will benefit from?

The Two Key Questions to Use Instead of Reprimanding Yourself Are:

4) What can I learn from this? *and*

5) How can I use this experience to move myself more quickly toward my objectives?

The first of these five questions is the most important because you can plug many different things into it. For instance, does this **program** work for me? Please ask yourself this question because the objective is to ensure your success. You now have the resources to do that, but you need to know what works and what does not.

Other things you may want to plug into this first key question are. Does this food plan work for me? Does this fitness plan work for me? Does this relationship work for me?

The second question is important because there are things in your life you think may work for you, but you may not benefit from the results.

The best example of this is cigarette smokers. If I ask, a smoker…"Does smoking work for you?" The image they will usually see initially is kicking back, relaxing, and enjoying their cigarette, so the initial answer is yes many times. If I then ask…"How do you feel, and will you benefit from the results of smoking?" This brings up a totally different picture, especially if you ask them to look at the results 10, 20, or 30 years from now.

You now see someone whose mouth looks like a puckered rectum; breathing has become difficult, and they have significantly shortened their quality of life. The third question is important because you cannot leave a blank spot in the subconscious mind. If you do not choose a replacement for an emotion, habit, or behavior, the subconscious will make one for you. The whole point of this program process is not to become who you are by accident, especially if it simply does not work.

Reprimanding yourself will keep you where you are and increase the weight of the anchor for what you do not want. Asking the last two questions will allow you to not only move away from making yourself feel bad but also use every experience in your life. **Nothing** in life is negative or useless if you fully understand how to speak to yourself about it.

Empowering Questions for My

Love

1) How can I make sure I continually and perpetually live in the light of love?

2) What do I need to do to be more loving toward my family, others, and myself?

3) What do I need to restructure that is keeping me from my perfect love?

4) What action do I need to take to ensure I perpetually live in the light of love?

5) What questions must I ask myself to ensure I live in the light of love?

6) What questions do I need to ask myself during prayer, meditation, or self-hypnosis?

7) How can I be more of a magnet for my perfect love?

8) What do I need to do to perceive all relationships as beneficial?

9) How can I stay focused on being grateful for what I have been blessed with?

10) How can I make every person a golden link in the chain of my good?

Love

11) What do I need to do to improve all my relationships?

12) How can I make sure my love never turns to hate or fear?

13) How can I be more receptive to all the love that surrounds me every day?

14) What do I need to do to perpetuate my perfect love?

15) What questions can I ask myself that will make me more of a magnet for my perfect love?

16) How can I improve my communication skills with the ones I love?

17) What am I willing to do to ensure my perfect love?

18) What action do I need to take to become more of a magnet for my perfect love?

19) What will happen today that will give me incredible pleasure for no reason?

20) How can I use every emotion and every life experience to move myself forward?

Empowering Questions for My

Love

21) What questions can I add to this list that will perpetually move me toward a powerful, empowering **Love**?

22)

23)

24)

25)

26)

27)

28)

29)

30)

Empowering Questions for My

Health

1) What action can I take to create positive change in my life every day?

2) How can I make sure I stay in the habit of restructuring things that do not work?

3) What do I need to do to maintain my excitement and enthusiasm for my fitness program every day?

4) Why do I feel so excited and enthusiastic about my fitness program?

5) How can I have more fun with my new eating, exercise, and other new habits?

6) Who or what do I need to process out my life that is keeping me from my perfect health?

7) How can I use everything in my life to move me toward my perfect health?

8) How can I ensure I only ask questions that work for me and move me quickly toward my food and fitness objectives?

9) What exercise do I enjoy enough to make it a permanent part of my weekly or daily workout routine?

10) Why do I love working out so much?

Empowering Questions for My
Health

11) What do I need to do to establish a permanent subconscious program that will continually and perpetually move me toward my perfect health?

12) What do I need to do to keep my emotional state from becoming erratic?

13) What am I the most excited about in my life?

14) What do I need to do to empower myself every day?

15) How can I ensure I only ask questions that will propel me toward my objectives?

16) What must I do to maintain a consistent exercise program?

17) What do I need to do to maintain my perfect health?

18) What is keeping me from my perfect health, and what do I need to do to restructure it or remove it from my life?

19) What questions do I need to ask myself every day to ensure I am continually moving toward my perfect health?

20) What foods will have the most positive effect on my emotional state?

Empowering Questions for My

Health

21) What questions can I add to this list that will perpetually move me toward my perfect **Health**?

22)

23)

24)

25)

26)

27)

28)

29)

30)

Empowering Questions for My

Wealth

1) What do I need to do to perceive every experience as positive?

2) How can I maximize my productivity every day?

3) What do I need to restructure that may be keeping me from my perfect wealth?

4) What do I need to do to define my objectives more clearly?

5) What do I need to do to maintain the focus of my objectives?

6) What subconscious programs do I need to change to move more quickly toward my objectives?

7) What action do I need to take to use every life experience as a stepping-stone toward my objectives?

8) What do I need to do to draw all things into my experience that will ensure my success?

9) How can I make sure I stay focused on the task at hand?

10) How can I eliminate confusion?

Empowering Questions for My

Wealth

11) How can I keep myself up, on, centered, and focused?

12) What do I need to do to become more of a magnet for my perfect wealth?

13) How can I increase my decision-making speed?

14) What do I need to do to perpetuate my perfect wealth?

15) What am I willing to do to ensure my perfect wealth?

16) How can I make sure I exploit my potential to the maximum every day?

17) What questions do I need to ask myself to clearly define the divine design of my life?

18) How can I make all things in my life work for me?

19) How can I use all events in my life as a stepping-stone to move me toward my objectives?

20) What questions do I need to ask myself daily to ensure I am constantly moving toward my objectives?

Empowering Questions for My
Wealth

21) What questions can I add to this list that will perpetually move me toward my perfect **Wealth**?

22)

23)

24)

25)

26)

27)

28)

29)

30)

Empowering Questions for My

Self-Image

1) How can I make sure I continually maintain a positive self-image?

2) What do I need to do to improve my sense of humor?

3) What do I need to do to consistently maintain my new self-image?

4) Why am I so happy?

5) What subconscious pictures or self-talk do I need to change to ensure a positive self-image?

6) How can I take greater control of my emotional state?

7) How can I make sure I thoroughly enjoy every day of my life?

8) What objectives do I need to set to ensure my happiness and maintain a powerful self-image?

9) What must I do to ensure all levels of consciousness are continually and perpetually integrated?

10) What do I need to do to maintain my emotional health?

Empowering Questions for My
Self-Image

11) What action do I need to take every day to maintain my emotional health?

12) What do I need to do to stay focused on all the positive aspects of my life?

13) What is the divine design of my life?

14) What do I need to do to fulfill the divine design of my life?

15) What do I need to do to make this a perfect day?

16) How can I make this the best day I have ever had?

17) What do I need to restructure that is keeping me from my most powerful self-image?

18) What am I willing to do to maintain my new self-image?

19) What do I need to do to perpetuate my new self-image?

20) What do I need to do to be closer to who I am instead of what I have learned?

Empowering Questions for My
Self-Image

21) What questions can I add to this list to help me maintain my new **Self-Image** of **Love, Health**, and **Wealth**?

22)

23)

24)

25)

26)

27)

28)

29)

30)

STEP 6

CRACKING THE GUT HEALTH CODE

Detox From Oxalates, Recover From Candida, Save Your Gallbladder,

Balance the Microbiota and Promote Health Span and Longevity

Disclaimer: *This page is provided for educational and informational purposes only. The information provided on this page should not be used to diagnose or treat a health problem or disease. Always seek the advice of your doctor or another qualified health provider regarding a medical condition. This content or its use creates no physician-patient relationship. For example, stopping an antidepressant or PTSD medication should only be done under the prescriber's supervision. This also applies to supplementation. If under the age of 18, nothing in this article should be implemented without the supervision of a parent or MD.*

Test Do Not Guess: The Top 5

If any of your numbers on the Burris Gut Health Checklist are a 5 or above consistently for more than 30 days, you must find a Functional Medicine MD who can order the following tests. After getting these tests, you will have enough data to correct your dysbiosis and rebalance the microbiota.

*Links to the following tests, tools, etc., are available at BurrisConnect.com with your free account.

1. Oxalaic Acid 24-Hour Urine Test: Even though there are results for oxalates in the NutrVal test, this one is considered the gold standard and the one I prefer. The test below was taken after being on a low-oxalate diet for 33 months. As you will see, the Reference

Range is 3.6 to 38 mg, and my score was 70.1. Oxalate dumping is, at best, erratic, so it is possible to get a false negative, but all three tests I took were out of range. Before taking a test, I recommend going low oxalate for at least 30 days. Low oxalate means less than 50 mg of oxalate daily.

Kelly Burris: Oxalate Acid 24-Hour Urine Test

2. **Vitamin D Test**: I did this test through Quest because it is oddly not included in the NutrVal Test. The test below was done when I took 20 to 40,000 IU of D3 daily. I have since reduced it to 10 to 20,000 IU daily and will get retested. D3 is critical to monitor, as you will find reading on.

Kelly Burris: Vitamin D Test

3. **Comprehensive Stool Sample**: Several labs will do this, but Genova has refined its testing over the last few years, and most insurance companies will cover it. You will want to discuss this with your MD. The bottom line is that you need to evaluate your microbiota comprehensively. My before and after are listed below.

Kelly Burris: Comprehensive Stool Test: 9-20

Kelly Burris: Comprehensive Stool Test: 9-22

4. **NutrEval**: NutrEval® is a blood and urine profile that evaluates over 125 biomarkers and assesses the body's functional need for 40 antioxidants, vitamins, minerals, essential fatty acids, amino acids, digestive support, and other select nutrients.

Kelly Burris: NutrEval

5. **1001 IgG Food Antibodies Profile**: The IgG and IgE Antibody Panels are blood tests that measure antibodies to commonly consumed foods and environmental allergens. Removal of the reactive foods often results in the resolution of symptoms. Of course, a carnivore diet is the ultimate elimination diet, but even so, it is essential to know which foods may be causing an issue. Your MD can also use this panel to determine if you should test for leaky gut. As you will see, I was well within range.

Kelly Burris: 1001 IgG Food Antibodies Profile

There are many more tests I would like to recommend, like an insulin test, SIBO test, and thyroid test, but these are the absolute musts. Your functional medicine practitioner can determine what other tests you may need based on these tests.

Stool Inspector

If you rated yourself a 5 or above on any of the questions on the Burris Gut Heath Checklist, you will need to inspect your stool regularly for oxalates, which are represented as tiny black specs, bile sludge, which will show up as emerald green chunks or stone shape and candida which is solid white, not to be confused with mucus which is translucent. You will need an LED flashlight and 2.25 power reading glasses or stronger to see the black oxalate specs.

Oxalate, Nutrition, Glycemic Index, Food Intolerances, and Measuring Tools

- **Oxalate.org**: It is critical that everyone has a full understanding of oxalates and measures their intake. This site will enable you to calculate your oxalate intake, which should not be more than 150 mg per day.
- **MyFoodData.com**: This site has several useful tools other than the stock nutritional tools. One I use is the Nutrient Ranking Tool. This tool enables you to select a nutrient and a food category to find the largest amount of that nutrient per the selected food. You can also simply select all. This is very useful when attempting to lower histidine. Histidine can be decarboxylated to histamine by histidine decarboxylase [5].
- **USDA**: Considered the gold standard for food data, but I prefer how MyFoodData.com is laid out.
- **GlycemicIndex.com**: The Glycemic Index enables you to determine how fast a food is turned into glucose. This is also important to determine possible inflammatory foods.
- **HowMany.wiki**: The primary tool I use on this site is the Volume to Weight Converter. This is an important tool when detoxing from oxalate.
- **Food Intolerances**: This App covers FODMAPs, Histamine, Lactose intolerance, Fructose intolerance, Sorbitol intolerance, Salicylate intolerance (or aspirin intolerance), Gluten intolerance, celiac disease, and Multiple Allergy Profiles.
- **Monash FODMAP App**: The Monash app is FODMAP only, but they do this very well.
- **High Lectin Foods**: This is a list by Dr. Gundry. There is no information on how he compiled this list, but Dr. Gundry is the super geek on lectins.
- **Bristol Stool Form Scale**: This scale establishes the guidelines for how your stool should look.

The Synergistic Trifecta of Gut Homeostasis

The synergistic trifecta of gut homeostasis consists of the gastrointestinal stem cells, intestinal mucosa, and gut microbiota. If any of these components is disrupted, it affects the other; therefore, all must be addressed simultaneously.

Gastrointestinal Stem Cells

The gastrointestinal stem cell produces all the adult cell lineages of the gastrointestinal mucosa and is thereby perceived as the most important regulatory element in gastrointestinal function [3]. Stem cell regeneration is the very foundation of recovering normal gut function. The endocannabinoid system (ECS) is a significant part of the stem cell equation because cannabinoid receptors are attached to the stem cells, and cannabinoid signaling regulates cell proliferation, differentiation, and survival [4].

Intestinal Mucosa

Inflammatory bowel disease is characterized by cycles of mucosal injury and ulceration [1]. My question is, can any bowel disorder that may lead to over one hundred forty autoimmune diseases happen without a mucosal injury? I believe that, in most cases, the answer is no. The medical literature regarding DBS/IBS is unclear. Still, it should be absolutely clear because one of the basic functions of the mucosal layer is the capacity to provide adequate containment of luminal microorganisms and molecules while preserving the ability to absorb nutrients [2].

The Microbiome and Gut Microbiota

Microbiome refers to all microorganisms and their genetic material living in the body, and microbiota refers to the populations of microorganisms in the body's various ecosystems (for example, the gut and skin microbiota). A completely clear indication of the microbes that dominate each system is still being discovered [151].

A breach in the mucosa can exacerbate immune reactions toward the microbiota. [2] This means that the immune system will attack the microbiota once the mucosa is breached. My Genova Comprehensive Stool Analysis indicated a very low diversity of bacteria on the first test.

With the importance of this trifecta made clear, I established a protocol to heal the gut and clear the remaining symptoms. Some people can heal by changing their diet, some can heal with probiotics, and others can heal without doing anything and letting the autonomic regenerative processes of the mucosa bring them back. However, an intervention is mandatory for those who have become ill or severely ill and cannot escape the disruption of the self-perpetuating cycle of the mucosa and microbiota. This cannot be stated emphatically enough, especially with anorexics who may have gotten to the point of not being able to eat because of severely damaged intestinal mucosa.

Oxalic Acid, Candida, Bile Sludge/Gallstones, and Histamine

Oxalate acid, candida, bile sludge/gallstones, and histamine represent a self-perpetuating mechanism for a disrupted microbiota leading to various disorders and diseases. People do not usually think of the liver and gallbladder when rebalancing the gut, but this is definitively part of the equation and must be effectively addressed.

Oxalic Acid

Oxalates are the most insidious of all plant toxins in that they are the only plant toxin that can accumulate in virtually every tissue of the body [6].

There are two primary ways to become poisoned from oxalates: endogenously (internal) via metabolism or exogenously (external) via the diet. Endogenous poisoning is usually caused by a rare genetic disorder.

Oxalic acid is a plant compound that is ubiquitous in the plant kingdom. It can damage tissue and ultimately slowly kill you if you engage in large amounts of superfoods such as spinach, chocolate, swiss chard, or almonds, among many others. However, several factors other than eating large amounts of this can make one vulnerable to this toxin embedded in your bones and tissues. Humans should not eat more than 150 mg of oxalates per day. This recommendation goes down to less than 50 mg per day if you have experienced kidney stones.

If you eat more than 150 mg of oxalates per day, the question is not whether you are poisoned but how poisoned you are.

Oxalate Poisoning Mechanisms

Escherichia coli are commonly found inside the nidus of calcium oxalate kidney stones and may play pivotal roles in stone genesis [7]. Candida albicans and Escherichia coli are also believed to be synergistic pathogens [8]. This is why some, like Great Plains Labs, believe candida causes excess oxalate accumulation. In other studies, a higher-than-usual concentration of oxalate was found to be inhibitory to many gut microbes, leading to dysbiosis and enabling commensal candida to be converted to its pathogenic form [9]. Once initiated, either mechanism becomes self-perpetuating and may eventually kill you unless you have a means of disrupting it. Death may not be directly from oxalate poisoning but from the resulting disorders and diseases from being poisoned. I suspect oxalates when a death is determined as a natural cause, especially if they are under the age of 70.

The question is, once either one of these mechanisms is initiated, how do you interrupt them and rebalance the microbiota? To be clear, oxalates are not the devil. Oxalates are produced in the liver as part of our metabolic processes. It binds with heavy metals and minerals and carries them out of the body. It only becomes problematic when there is an excess accumulation.

What Makes You Vulnerable to Exogenous Oxalate Poisoning

- Stress
- Antibiotics
- Alcohol
- Pharmaceutical or Illicit Drugs
- Ingesting Excessive Amounts of Oxalate Rich Foods (More than 150 mg per day)
- Inflammation
- Inflammatory Foods

Systemic Manifestations of Oxalate Disorders [10]

Joints

- Arthritis

- Chondrocalcinosis of the metacarpophalangeal and metatarsophalangeal joints

- Spinal stenosis

- Synovitis

- Tenosynovitis

- Bursitis

Kidneys

- Acute tubular necrosis
- Interstitial fibrosis
- Nephrocalcinosis
- Kidney stones

Heart

- Arrhythmias
- Diastolic dysfunction
- Valvular abnormalities
- Impaired ejection fraction
- Infiltrative process

Skin

- Livedo reticularis
- Acrocyanosis
- Papules and nodules on the face and digits
- Non-healing ulcers

Eyes

- Retinal oxalate deposition

Nerve and muscle

- Axon loss and Demyelination
- Polyradiculoneuropathies

Teeth

- Periodontitis
- Jaw bone and root resorption
- Dental mobility
- Bone marrow
- Erythropoietin stimulating agent-resistant anemia

Bones

- Fractures

- Pseudofractures

- Sclerosis

- Cystic bone changes

- Dense metaphyseal bands

- Increased bone density

Other Reported Oxalate Dumping Symptoms

- Gallbladder and Liver Stones

- Bile Sludge

- Candida Overgrowth

- Hallucinations

- Paranoia

- Poor Sleep

- Suicidality (Suicidal Thoughts)

- Exhibited symptoms of ALS, Parkinson's, Alzheimer's, Aphasia, and Multiple Sclerosis

- Vertigo

- Neuromyelitis Optica

- Skin Peeling off Lips

- Increased Gait Abnormalities

- Axon Loss and Demyelination

- Arrhythmias

- Periodontitis

- Increased Chronic Fatigue

- Increased Brain Fog

- Plaque Build-Up on Lower Front Teeth

- Itchy Skin

- Large Amounts of Oxalate Crystals From My Eyes

- Excessive Ear Wax

- Dry Cough

- Itchy Throat

- Constipation

- Stiff Neck

- Ringing in the Ears (Tinnitus)

- Dizziness, Poor Balance

- Hyper Sensitivity to Light, Noise, and Odors

- Interstitial Cystitis (Bladder Pain)

- Enlarged Prostrate

- ED

Oxalate induces breast cancer: Chronic exposure of breast epithelial cells to oxalate promotes the transformation of breast cells from normal to tumor cells, inducing the expression of a proto-oncogen such as c-fos and proliferation in breast cancer cells. Furthermore, oxalate has a carcinogenic effect when injected into the mammary fat pad in mice, generating highly malignant and undifferentiated tumors with the characteristics of fibrosarcomas of the breast. As oxalates seem to promote these differences, it is expected that a significant reduction in the incidence of breast cancer tumors could be reached if it were possible to control oxalate production or its carcinogenic activity [160].

Even though I had many of the symptoms listed above, I had many more listed below. This is also why I list oxalate dumping as the first consideration when initiating a flexible carnivore diet.

Oxalate Dumping

Oxalate dumping or purging is a release of oxalates stored in body tissue when the body detects that no oxalates are being consumed. If poisoned with oxalates, it is recommended that you slowly reduce the amount of oxalate you are eating by 10 percent per week. Planning which oxalate foods you will leave in to slow down this process is essential. I ultimately found that 3 rounded tablespoons of organic sprouted buckwheat flour at approximately 8 milligrams of oxalate per tablespoon were adequate most of the time. To curb heart palpations and bladder pain during a heavy purge, I would add a tablespoon of organic cacao, which is 25 milligrams of oxalate. The biggest takeaway from this process is that there is no linearity to the purging process. It can occur any time of the day or night and at varying intensity levels. I found myself continually adjusting the amount of oxalate I was eating to match the intensity of the dump to reduce the symptoms. To call oxalate dumping a brutal, horrifying, nightmarish process would be a profound understatement. Because oxalates, candida, and bile sludge are self-perpetuating mechanisms, it was initially impossible to tell which one was causing the symptoms. However, I decided to focus on candida infection and bile sludge and found out that oxalate dumping was not the direct cause of the horrendous symptoms.

One cannot fully appreciate this until you have lived through it, and even then, it isn't easy to get your head around the fact that the foods you were told were healthy superfoods your entire life is doing this to you.

Probiotics have been used to attempt to facilitate the breakdown of oxalates, but the results have been inconsistent [11-12]. Oxalobactor are believed to be the primary gut bacteria for breaking down oxalates and one of the first to be destroyed when under stress or taking antibiotics.

However, Oxalobactor was intact on my comprehensive stool test. I eventually tracked down the worst of my symptoms to **Candida** and **Bile Sludge**, both resulting from oxalate dumping.

Candida

Candida Albicans is the most common form of candida and can not be controlled until you get oxalates stored in your body within range. As stated above, candida and oxalates are self-perpetuating mechanisms. This is one of the primary reasons so many people report that it keeps coming back. This is not to say that medications like nystatin or antifungals will not work because they may if oxalates are not part of the equation, but this is not the case most of the time. One can have a candida flare-up without oxalates, but it is highly unlikely that it is not part of the equation if you are poisoned with oxalates.

For Women: Recurrent Vaginal Candidiasis

If C Albicans were cultured from the vagina, it was always found in the stool. Conversely, if it was not isolated from the stool, it was never found in the vagina. These data are presented as an explanation for the recurrent nature of Candida vaginitis. Thus, a cure for vaginitis would not be possible without prior eradication of C. albicans from the gut [13]. It is estimated that 75% of females will have a yeast infection at some point in their lives. This completely discredits the notion that yeast overgrowth is primarily found in immune-compromised people.

Bringing the Microbiota Back Into Balance

With severe oxalate poisoning and consistent candida flare-ups, I tried everything except medication, and most of it worked initially, but candida was very good at adapting. However, there are 3 things that candida cannot adapt to: starvation via fasting, glycine, and niacin. After trying every form of fasting, I initially tried a 3-44 fasting schedule. This translates to 3 44-hour fasts per week. It took about 9 days to kick in, but I passed large amounts of yeast for 4 months once it did. Even though this protocol was effective, it was unsustainable, so I switched to a 24 to 29-hour fast every other day. Keep in mind that you will have to maintain this protocol for as long as you are infected with oxalates, which were years, as in my case. I also found this unsustainable, so I implemented glycine and niacin and initiated a 36 to 44-hour fast once per week with a 72-hour fast once per month. Even if I missed a fast, the niacin and glycine maintained the yeast die off. Ultimately, one must experiment to find a fasting protocol that works.

Following are the five most potent candida killers I have found.

Top 6 Candida Killers

1. Seaweed: The Ultimate Candida Killer

I used the full sheet of Roasted Sushi Nori seaweed and found it not to be noticeably effective at 2 to 4 sheets; however, at 8 to 10 sheets at one meal, it was very effective. This amount always initiated a massive candida die-off, and this is consistent with the latest research.

Thus far the C. albicans has not been able to adapt to the seaweed. Seaweed is so effective that one would want to start slow and work up to a dose that works.

One virulence factor of C. albicans is biofilm formation. The ability to create biofilm makes C. albicans more tolerant to commercial antifungal agents. The highest inhibitory effect was recorded in a fungus culture treated with a seaweed concentration of 25% at exposure for 24 hours. Seaweed G. verrucosa extract contained steroids, terpenoids, and tannins that effectively inhibited biofilm formation by C. albicans at a concentration of 25% after exposure for 24 hours [157].

2. Glycine: A Supreme Candida Killer

Candida albicans cannot adapt to therapeutic amounts of glycine. This is a critical factor because, as stated earlier, a candida infection will be chronic as long as one is infected with oxalates, and an oxalate infection can go on for years, as it has with me.

Another major issue, in my opinion, is that medications like nystatin only clear the gut of candida, and that is if it works at all. If your infection is invasive or systemic, as it was for me, it will not affect the rest of the body. Glutathione Reductase promoted fungal clearance and suppressed inflammation during systemic candida albicans infection in mice [105]. This is why I do not discount all mouse models. I found that therapeutic amounts of glycine, which increases glutathione, were so effective I had to cut back several times because the candida die-off was so extreme. Glutathione breaks down the biofilm that protects the candida overgrowth [105].

This is critical because a candida biofilm also protects multiple viruses, including herpes simplex 1 (cold sore) and SARS-CoV-2 (severe acute respiratory syndrome coronavirus 2) [146].

Glycine Dosing and Toxicity

In a study on OCD and body dysmorphic disorder, .6 to .8 grams per kilogram a day was used over 5 years with only improvements in these disorders [106]. Per my weight, .8 grams per kilogram would be 61 grams per day.

Warning: Even though Glycine is well tolerated, it is so good at killing candida (via glutathione) and other pathogens that just taking 30 grams a day caused the worst candida die-off I have ever experienced. Glutathione has a solid reputation for being the master antioxidant, but I did not realize that it also kills the fungus that creates the oxidants. I took 6 grams of glycine per day before increasing it, and I did not notice any die-off. Eighteen grams and above caused significant to massive candida die-offs, so I settled on 18 grams (one tablespoon).

3. Niacin (Niacinamide)

NAM (niacinamide) exhibited significant antifungal activity against C. albicans, including fluconazole-resistant isolates. NAM could also effectively suppress biofilm formation. In addition, NAM exhibited antifungal activity against non-Candida albicans species and Cryptococcus neoformans. The antifungal activity of NAM was further confirmed in a mouse model of disseminated candidiasis. These findings suggested that NAM might exhibit antifungal activities by affecting cell wall organization [144].

3. Olive Oil

- **Oleuropein** constitutes over seventy percent of the phenolic compounds in olive oil and olive leaf. This is why it has gained a reputation as the best anti-inflammatory, antioxidant, antiviral, antimicrobial, anticancer, anti-aging, anti-candida, antiparasitic, and neuroprotective compound [14].
- **Oleocanthal** rapidly and selectively induces cancer cell death. As with Oleuropein, Oleocanthal is an effective anti-inflammatory along with several other attributes, including Anti-Alzheimer Agent, Anticarcinogenic Agent, and Cardioprotective Agent [15].
- **Hydroxytyrosol** reduces oxidative stress and inflammation, thus positively altering the key components of metabolic syndrome [16]. Metabolic syndrome is a cluster of conditions that occur together, increasing your risk of heart disease, stroke, and type 2 diabetes. These conditions include increased blood pressure, high blood sugar, excess body fat around the waist, and abnormal cholesterol or triglyceride levels.

An in vitro study showed that olive leaf aqueous extracts destroyed 15% of C. Albicans within 24 hours [155].

What to Look for When Purchasing Olive Oil

- **Organic**
- **Extra Virgin**
- **First Cold Pressed**
- **Sourced From a Single Region**
- **Use by Date: 1 Year Out Preference**
- **DOP/POD**: DOP stands for "Denominazione di Origine Protetta" in Italy or PDO "Protected Designation of Origin." For a particular area to be awarded the PDO/DOP status, it must produce an outstanding olive oil and have a good reputation.
- For olive oil to qualify for the PDO/DOP name and logo, it must be grown, produced, and bottled in the designated area, but it must also meet strict requirements in terms of

varietals, method of production, and overall quality. The bottom line is whether you want the best DOP or POD designation look.

- **Counterfeit Olive Oil**: If you want a less expensive olive oil and are unsure about the purity you are using, go to https://www.aboutoliveoil.org/certified-olive-oil-list to see if it has been tested for purity.

4. Crustless, Unsweetened Pumpkin Pie

- **Pumpkin Puree**: Pumpkin has been shown to be antimicrobial, anti-inflammatory, antiparasitic, anticarcinogenic, antioxidant, antidiabetic, hypotensive, and hepatoprotective [18]. There is a concern for high levels of lectins in pumpkins, but these are concentrated in the rhine and seeds of the pumpkin when you get organic canned pumpkin puree.
- **Cinnamon**: Cinnamon oil is effective against nearly 50% of the Candida isolates [19].
- **Cloves**: Clove oil possesses strong antifungal activity against opportunistic fungal pathogens such as Candida albicans, Cryptococcus neoformans, Aspergillus fumigatus, etc. [20].
- **Ginger**: Ginger extract successfully inhibited biofilm formation by A. baumannii, B. cereus, C. krusei, and C. Albicans. The minimum inhibitory biofilm concentrations (MIBCs) of ginger extract for fungi strains (C. krusei and C. Albicans) were greater than those of fluconazole and nystatin [21].
- **Nutmeg**: Nutmeg (Myristica fragrans) was effective against all endodontic pathogens, including C. Albicans [22].

Crustless Unsweetened Pumpkin Pie Recipe

- One 15-ounce can of organic pumpkin puree
- One tablespoon of pumpkin spice
- 3 whole eggs or 6 yolks
- ¾ of a cup of heavy cream

Thoroughly mix the first 3 ingredients before adding the heavy cream to keep the spice from clumping, then stir again. I use a 9-inch glass pie pan and rub it down with butter or Ghee, so it is easy to clean. Next, preheat the oven or toaster oven to 350 degrees and bake for 30 minutes. Let it cool for 20 minutes after taking it out of the oven.

5. Coconut Oil

- VCO is an antimicrobial and antifungal [24].
- VCO is an antibacterial and antiviral [25].
- VCO (virgin coconut oil) significantly reduces plaque and plaque-induced gingivitis [23].

Bile Sludge, Gallstones, and Liver Stones

Bile sludge is thought to be a precursor to gallstones and liver stones. I have experienced both, and I can tell you that this is indeed accurate. The bottom line is that bile sludge and gallstone composition were not understood until 2020 when advanced spectroscopic techniques were used to confirm that gallstones were composed of oxalate. There are many types of gallstones, but all have at least some oxalate [26].

Bile Sludge and Gallstone Symptoms

The most common symptomatic manifestation of gallstones is episodic upper abdominal pain. Characteristically, this pain is severe and located in the epigastrium and/or the right upper quadrant. The onset is relatively abrupt and often awakens the patient from sleep. The pain is steady in intensity, may radiate to the upper back, be associated with nausea, and lasts for hours to up to a day. Dyspeptic symptoms of indigestion, belching, bloating, abdominal discomfort, heartburn, and specific food intolerance are common in persons with gallstones but are probably unrelated to the stones and frequently persist after surgery [34]. This is only one of the many reasons surgery does not make sense for most people.

Effects of Bile Acids on Neurological Function

Bile acids are synthesized from cholesterol and are known to be involved with the emulsification and digestion of dietary lipids and fat-soluble vitamins. Outside of this role, bile acids can act as cell signaling effectors. Bile acids are the end products of cholesterol metabolism and can contribute to hepatic, intestinal, and metabolic disorders [27].

Neuromyelitis Optica

Neuromyelitis Optica is one of the neurological autoimmune conditions linked to bile acids [28]. This was one of the multitudes of symptoms I had and recovered from. Another theory is that oxalate crystals travel down the optic nerve from the brain. This is why I am still flushing oxalate crystals from my eyes with water up to 10 times a day. The medical literature does not make the connection between oxalate and this condition nor how to reduce bile sludge effectively, which I will get into below.

The Nerve Repair Stack

- B1: Benfotiamine
- R-Alpha Lipoic Acid
- B6: Prydoxial-5-Phosphate
- B9: Folate
- B12: Mythelcobalmin
- L-Citrulline
- Carnitine: I do not supplement this as I believe I get enough from meat.
- Check with your Functional Medicine MD to determine the amount of each supplement to take.

Histamine

Histamine is an organic nitrogenous compound involved in local immune responses, regulates physiological functions in the gut, and acts as a neurotransmitter for the brain, spinal cord, and uterus.

Oxalate dumping and candida die-off cause the mast cells to release histamine. This, in conjunction with eating high histidine foods, can cause what appears to be histamine intolerance. I say "what appears to be" because virtually no MDs understand the process of oxalate dumping and the results it produces; therefore, they label it histamine intolerance. In my opinion, it is histamine overload if you are dealing with oxalate dumping and candida die-off. Either way, histamine must be considered an essential piece of the oxalate candida equation.

The first thing that is prescribed is antihistamines, and this is usually without an accurate diagnosis. Histamine intolerance or overload symptoms are similar to some of the symptoms of oxalate dumping and candida die-off, so it just adds to the overall malaise.

Diamine oxidase (DAO) is the enzyme that breaks down histamine, and I felt it was better to add a food high in DAO and reduce the amount of histidine I was eating [29]. Beef kidney is high in DAO, so I took it in freeze-dried capsule form. I was able to tell the difference, which sold me on the idea of freeze-dried animal organs. You do want to be careful about reducing histidine because it has been found to improve mental fatigue, cognitive performance, and sleep disruption [30].

The Flexible Carnivore Diet: The Best Diet for Candida, Oxalate Poisoning, Inflammation, and Autoimmune Disease

The flexible Carnivore Diet is primarily meat-based. The Flexible designation of this diet is because it is not purely carnivore. This is because when the body detects low or no oxalates coming in, it will begin purging the oxalates stored in the body. This is why it is important to come off them slowly because oxalates are much more toxic coming out than going in. Also, it is extremely unpleasant when you add candida die-off and bile sludge caused in part by the dumping of oxalates into this equation. The bottom line is to find a fasting protocol and flexible carnivore diet that works for you.

Working up to this must be implemented slowly because if you are severely infected with oxalates candida and bile sludge, the malaise from this combination can be catastrophic.

What is the objective of this food? You must ask this question about any food you eat outside the carnivore diet. Following are the non-carnivore foods I kept and why.

- **Lemon Juice**: I kept the lemon juice because the citrate helps break down the oxalates, and I use it to take shots of olive oil.
- **Seaweed**: My metabolic test indicated low thyroid hormone, and my voice quality was bad. Seaweed is rich in iodine.

- **Sprouted Organic Pumpkin Seeds**: Along with being antiparasitic and having a good mineral profile, specifically a good balance of copper and zinc, pumpkin seeds seem to assist digestion. This is another high-lectin food; however, that must be sprouted.
- **Organic Unsweetened Shredded Coconut**: I avoid the reduced-fat versions of this. Shredded coconut is the most potent parasite killer I have found and goes great with pumpkin pie.
- **Crustless Unsweetened Pumpkin Pie**: A good candida killer; however, candida can adapt.

Temporary High Oxalate Foods for Reduction of Oxalate Dumping Symptoms

- **Sprouted Organic Buckwheat Flour**: Buckwheat is not a grain but a fruit with a low glycemic index and a good mineral profile. I used a little over an ounce daily to take down the oxalate dumping symptoms. Sprouting deactivates the lectins and phytic acid.
- **Raw Organic Cacao**: I used this to increase my oxalate intake to significantly lower symptoms. I only used this when necessary because virtually all cacao has lead, cadmium, and high oxalate concentrations. Consumer Reports wrote an article titled "Lead and Cadmium Could Be in Your Dark Chocolate," in which they outline chocolate bars with the least and most lead and cadmium. I used a powdered form of cacao and found Navitas to have the lowest cadmium and lead at 0.13mcg/g and 0.07mcg/g, respectively.

Acclimation to this diet can take days to weeks to months, and you could very well heal yourself while implementing this. Unfortunately, this was not the case for me, but I do not expect everyone to be as severely infected as I was.

Fasting

Never engage a fast without consulting with your MD. There are many fasting derivations. The one I am addressing here is ADF, or Alternate Day Fasting because it has been found to be safe in several studies. It has, in fact, not only been proven for eating disorders but also enabled improvement [31-32]. Anorexia is an exception to this if you are below a safe body fat percentage. Any diet protocol, in this case, must be under the supervision of your MD. ADF is the most studied fasting protocol I have found, and it has benefits that go far beyond killing yeast and rebalancing the microbiota. Fast Like a Girl is a good book for females wanting to start fasting.

A Short List of Other ADF Benefits [33]

- ADF showed statistically significant reductions in weight and body mass index
- ADF showed significant differences in terms of total cholesterol
- ADF showed significant differences in low-density lipoprotein
- ADF showed significant differences in triglycerides
- ADF showed significant differences in fat mass
- ADF showed significant differences in lean mass

- ADF showed significant differences in systolic and diastolic blood pressure
- ADF had the same effect compared with the control group in aspects of high-density lipoprotein homeostasis model assessment-insulin resistance and fasting blood sugar

Conclusions: This meta-analysis suggests that ADF is a viable diet strategy for weight loss and substantially improves disease risk indicators in obese or normal-weight people.[33]

Inflammation is at the core of virtually all diseases, and digesting food is an inflammatory process. This is why fasting is fundamental if you suffer from any digestive disorder.

Intermittent and Extended Fasting with the Flexible Carnivore Diet

You must get approval from your MD before starting a fasting regimen, especially if you take any medications. Implementation of this diet requires that you start slow with intermittent fasting. This means choosing an eating window of 8, 6, 4, or 24 hours. Anything past 24 hours is considered extended fasting. I started with a 6-hour eating window and then moved to a 4-hour window called the warrior diet. I then initiated ADF once per week, then twice weekly. I was 30 hours into the second 44-hour fast at one point, and it felt like I was experiencing multiple organ failures, so I cut it short. However, I did pick it up the following day and kept going.

Fasting is tricky if you are poisoned with oxalates, and you have candida overgrowth because fasting accelerates the exit of the oxalates from the body and causes candida to die off. The malaise can be pretty extreme, so you must closely listen to your body and continually adjust what you are doing. I ate about 25 mg of oxalate daily to slow down the dumping, and I had to double it after starting this diet. Within two months, I was back down to 25 milligrams. I discovered that candida die-off and bile sludge symptoms were much more severe than oxalate, so I stayed focused on fasting.

Fasting and Flexible Carnivore Considerations

- Oxalate Dumping
- Candida Die-Off
- Bile Sludge
- Fat to Protein Ratio
- Mineral Balance
- Supplements
- Glycine Balance
- Water

Fat to Protein Ratio

Even though there are some carbs in this diet, I still found it necessary to pay attention to how much fat I ate. If constipation is an issue, then I was not eating enough fat. I did not eat just any fat. Vegetable oils (grain oils) or seed oils were not a consideration, with flax seed oil being the exception.

Top 5 Fats

- First, Cold-Pressed Organic Extra Virgin Olive Oil DPO/PDO Designation
- Organic Ghee from Grass-Fed Cows
- Organic Virgin Coconut Oil
- Organic Tallow from Grass-Fed Cows
- Organic Butter from Grass-Fed Cows, if Tolerated

There are many more good ones; these just happen to be the ones I use.

Ending a Fast: Addressing Constipation, Killing Candida, and Flushing the Liver and Gallbladder

There are three issues olive oil effectively addresses when detoxing from oxalate poisoning. At the top of the list is constipation. This is a critical issue because you do not want oxalates and candida die off to linger in the intestines. Second on the list is olive oil. Olive oil is an anti-microbial and assists glycine in eradicating candida overgrowth. Third on this list is keeping the bile flowing in the liver and gallbladder. Keeping the liver and gallbladder flushed and free of sludge greatly assists digestion and preventing gallstones. Olive oil has many other attributes, but these three are critical.

Olive Oil Dosing

1-2 ounces for maintenance

3-4 ounces for flushing the liver and gallbladder

3-4 ounces for prevention of constipation up to 2 times daily

My olive oil schedule is as follows. Two hours before breaking a fast, I take 3 ounces of olive oil and an equal amount of organic lemon juice. If constipation is an issue, I will do 3 ounces in the morning and 3 ounces at night before bed.

Getting Help with the Carnivore Diet

If you need help getting started with a carnivore diet, you can find a coach at revero.com.

Senescence Autophagy and Apoptosis

It is important to have a fundamental understanding of senescence, autophagy, and apoptosis, especially as they relate to fasting.

Senescence cells are damaged cells that secrete proinflammatory cytokines, which stimulate the immune system and can cause inflammation, leading to the damage of other cells. Senescent cells accumulate in various tissues with aging and at sites of pathogenesis in many chronic diseases and conditions, including metabolic dysregulation, stem cell dysfunction, aging phenotypes, chronic diseases, geriatric syndromes, and loss of resilience. Senescent cells can also stimulate the regeneration of new cells, which creates a double-edged sword

[152]. This, in my opinion, is why pharmaceuticals used to kill senescent cells should be closely examined.

Immunosenescence is what it sounds like, which is the slow death of immune cells. Prolonged Fasting kills senescent cells, which stimulate the generation of new cells.

Autophagy and Apoptosis

Autophagy means self-eat, and regarding fasting, the body uses old and damaged stem cells and, in theory, senescent cells as fuel. This is why age, disease, and health biomarkers improve. It is impossible to know if autophagy extends one's life, but it can extend one's health. The loss of autophagy is enough to drive cellular, tissue, and organismal dysfunction with detrimental effects on health and lifespan; by contrast, boosting autophagy has the opposite effects [152].

I saw autophagy right before my eyes after suffering a massive oxalate dump and ended up with a cobweb of floaters in my right eye. I immediately did a 72-hour fast and saw most of the floaters disappear. A 48-hour fast had little effect on the floaters in my other eye. This is why I also believe that meaningful autophagy only occurs between 36 and 72 hours.

Apoptosis is programmed cell death independent of cell damage [153]. However, both senescent cells and apoptosis are affected by fasting [154].

Mineral Balance: The Synergistic 4

Magnesium, potassium, sodium, and calcium work synergistically. Oxalic acid binds with heavy metals and minerals. This is why close attention must be paid to this balance. It is difficult to accurately measure calcium and magnesium because the body will pull these two minerals into the bloodstream from bone to keep them in balance. The question regarding magnesium is, do I sleep well, and are my dreams clear and vivid? If the answer is no, sufficient magnesium may be an issue. 'Approximately 50% of Americans consume less than the Estimated Average Requirement (EAR) for magnesium, and some age groups consume substantially less'.[103]

Other comments on this diet suggest no issues regarding mineral balance, supplementation, or glycine balance. Everyone seems to agree on the fat-to-protein ratio and water and salt. Nonetheless, I addressed all these issues. I had been battling candida for over a decade and was suffering from several mineral and vitamin deficiencies. Magnesium and calcium are based on RDA sodium, and potassium is based on AI (adequate intake). You will need to look up your requirements, as the following numbers are based on my gender and age.

- **Magnesium**: 420 mg per day
- **Potassium**: 4,700 mg per day
- **Sodium**: 1,500 mg per day
- **Calcium**: 1,000 per day

Supplements

I do not listen to any recommendations regarding supplements because it always comes down to Test: Do Not Guess.

Top 10 Gut Health Supplements

1. **Glycine**: Glycine is known as the master antioxidant, but as I found, it is much more, including the ultimate candida killer—more on this under Amino Acids: A Complex Picture.

2. **Tryptophan**: Tryptophan is the sole precursor of peripherally and centrally produced serotonin [101]. A Tryptophan-deficient diet induces gut microbiota dysbiosis and increased systemic inflammation in aged mice—more on this under Amino Acids: A Complex Picture [102].

3. **L-Citrulline**: L-Citrulline is a precursor for arginine and nitric oxide. Diminished bioavailability of nitric oxide (NO), the gaseous signaling molecule involved in the regulation of numerous vital biological functions, contributes to the development of multiple age and lifestyle-related risk factors and diseases, including hypertension, atherosclerosis, insulin resistance, type 2 diabetes (T2D), and cardiovascular disease [104]. This critical molecule begins to drop off by age 40.

4. **Magnesium Citrate**: The enzymatic process of vitamin D requires magnesium along with approximately 300 other enzymatic processes, so I had to increase this mineral. Citrate assists in breaking down oxalate, but there are many forms of magnesium.

The magnesium deception: All magnesium has to be bound with something, and most manufacturers include what it is bound to as part of the milligram rating. This can be deceiving as only about 16% of it is elemental magnesium. The bulk magnesium I recommend tells you how much elemental magnesium you get per serving. If magnesium does not clearly state the amount of elemental magnesium, I would not purchase it.

5. **Potassium Citrate**: I get this in bulk and take a teaspoon per day, but my potassium was still borderline.

6. **R-Alpha Lipoic Acid**: I take 600 mg daily based on my NutrVal. The R indicates it is the natural version, which is more bioavailable. ALA and B12 compete for the same pathway, so this takes some adjusting. It is estimated that taking R-Alpha Lipoic Acid on an empty stomach increases bioavailability by 40%, so I take this first thing in the morning before any food, along with vitamin C.

7. **B Complex**: I was low on B1, B2, B3, and B6, so I changed my B vitamin protocol. I am now using B Complex, along with Benfotiamine (B1), B2, and nicotinic acid, which is a form of B3 and B6.

Warning: Because of the large number of scams involving NMN, I can only recommend three brands: ProHealth Longevity, Renue by Science, and Do Not Age.

8. **Vitamin C**: At the time I took the NutrVal test, I was taking 500 milligrams of vitamin C, and it was still low, so I increased it to 1 gram.

Ascorbate: This is the natural form of vitamin C and the one you want to take.

Ascorbic Acid: This is the synthetic version of vitamin C and the one you want to avoid.

9. **Vitamin D3 K2**: Sports Research is plant-based, and the best price is at Costco. Just this alone is worth the Costco membership.

10. **Krill Oil**: Krill oil is more bioavailable than fish oil. Of the two PUFAs Within the brain, DHA (docosahexaenoic acid) is the major omega 3, comprising about 10–15% of all fatty acids and over 50% of all brain PUFA (Polyunsaturated fatty acids) [12].

    For this reason, DHA was thought to be the most important regarding neurological function, but a recent study found that EPA (eicosapentaenoic acid) was responsible for increased CNS remyelination. The myelin sheath is what protects nerve cells and what becomes damaged in MS [100].

Amino Acids: A Complex Picture

Amino acids (AAs) are organic compounds containing amino and acid groups. Proteinogenic AAs serve as substrates for protein synthesis in animal cells and occur naturally as L-AAs (the molecules used to produce proteins in the human body), except for glycine [127].

Enhanced intake of most amino acid supplements may not be risk-free and can cause a number of detrimental side effects. This is why I have isolated the amino acids I use and no longer use Collagen Peptides.

The 22 amino acids that comprise proteins include [130]

Alanine

Arginine

Asparagine

Aspartic Acid

Cysteine

Glutamic acid

Glutamine

Glycine

Histidine

Isoleucine

Leucine

Lysine

Methionine

Phenylalanine

Proline

Serine

Threonine

Tryptophan

Tyrosine

Valine

Selenocysteine

Pyrrolysine (not used in human protein synthesis)

Of these 22 amino acids, nine amino acids are essential

Phenylalanine

Valine

Tryptophan

Threonine

Isoleucine

Methionine

Histidine

Leucine

Lysine

The non-essential, also known as dispensable amino acids, can be excluded from a diet. The human body can synthesize these amino acids using only the essential amino acids. For most physiological states in a healthy adult, the above nine amino acids are the only essential amino acids. However, amino acids like arginine and histidine may be considered conditionally essential because the body cannot synthesize them in sufficient quantities during certain physiological periods of growth, including pregnancy, adolescent growth, or recovery from trauma. [104] Some amino acids may be needed in larger amounts than the body makes, such as glycine, the most important amino acid.

Amino Acid Uses Toxicity and Side Effects

Glycine

Detailed assessment of all possible sources of glycine shows that synthesis from serine accounts for more than 85% of the total and that the amount of glycine available from synthesis, about 3 g/day, together with that available from the diet, in the range of 1.5-3.0 g/day, may fall significantly short of the amount needed for all metabolic uses, including collagen synthesis by about 10 g per day for a 70 kg human. This result supports earlier suggestions in the literature that glycine is a semi-essential amino acid and that it should be taken as a nutritional supplement to guarantee a healthy metabolism [109].

Glycine has also been suggested as a conditionally essential amino acid. In metabolic disorders associated with obesity, type 2 diabetes (T2DM), and non-alcoholic fatty liver disease (NAFLD), lower circulating glycine levels have been consistently observed, and clinical studies suggest the existence of beneficial effects induced by glycine supplementation.

I consider glycine the most important and versatile amino acid for the following reasons.

1. Data suggest glycine may support mitochondrial function independently of NAC [108].

2. Glycine is a precursor for glutathione [108].

3. Glutathione Reductase promoted fungal clearance and suppressed inflammation during systemic candida albicans infection in mice [105]. In other words, it is the ultimate candida killer.

4. Glycine protects human intestinal epithelial cells against oxidative damage [116].

5. Glycine suppresses kidney calcium oxalate crystal depositions [110].

6. Glycine is now recognized as a relevant plasma marker for metabolic diseases associated with obesity [117].

7. Acute glycine supplementation (5 g/day) improved insulin response and glucose tolerance [111].

8. Glycine supplementation was attributed to improved glutathione synthesis and antioxidant protection [111].

9. Oral supplementation with glycine reduces oxidative stress in patients with metabolic syndrome, improving their systolic blood pressure [112].

10. High glycine concentration increases collagen synthesis [113].

11. Acute glycine deficiency could be an important cause of osteoarthritis [113].

12. Glycine extends lifespan in worms, mice, and rats [114].

13. Glycine also improves aspects of health in mammalian models of age-related disease [114].

14. Glycine Regulates Mitochondria-Mediated Autophagy [118].

15. Glycine may prolong life by inducing autophagy and mimicking methionine restriction [114].

16. Glycine reduces oxidative stress in patients with metabolic syndrome, improving their systolic blood pressure [115].

Glycine Dosing

In a study on OCD and body dysmorphic disorder, .6 to .8 grams per kilogram a day was used over 5 years with only improvements in these disorders [106]. Another study concluded that a dose of 15 grams of glycine per day is the highest dose well tolerated in adult humans [112]. My takeaway from these studies is that 15 grams per day is a good maintenance dose, and above 15 grams would be considered a therapeutic dose.

Tryptophan (TRP)

Experimental research has shown that L-tryptophan, as the sole precursor of serotonin, plays an important role in brain serotonin synthesis and is involved in mood, behavior, and cognition. Furthermore, clinical trials have provided some initial evidence of L-tryptophan's efficacy for treating psychiatric disorders, particularly when combined with other therapeutic agents [120].

In the bloodstream, tryptophan competes with other large neutral amino acids such as histidine, isoleucine, leucine, methionine, phenylalanine, threonine, tyrosine, and valine for the BBB transporter [120]. This is why I do not use any other amino acids when I supplement with tryptophan.

I consider tryptophan the second most important amino acid for the following reasons.

1. TRP is an essential proteinogenic amino acid used to treat depression and insomnia [107].

2. TRP increases the synthesis of serotonin (5-hydroxytryptamine)—a neurotransmitter known to regulate neuronal circuits that control sleep and mood [107].

3. Next to its role as a neurotransmitter, serotonin is the precursor of melatonin, modulates gut and immune functions, and plays a role in hemostasis [107].

4. TRP supplementation has been employed as a potential treatment for depression and sleep disturbances since the early 1960s [107].

5. There is considerable evidence for the beneficial effects of TRP on mood and social behavior [107].

6. TRP can reduce aggression in schizophrenic patients while increasing agreeableness in people with a tendency to irritability or aggression [107].

7. A Tryptophan-Deficient Diet Induces Gut Microbiota Dysbiosis and Increases Systemic Inflammation in Aged Mice [119].

8. TRP is a constituent of protein synthesis [121].

9. Sole precursor for serotonin synthesis. [120].

10. TRP affects mood, and women may be more vulnerable to the mood-lowering effects of tryptophan depletion than men. [120].

11. Dopamine, norepinephrine, and beta-endorphin have been shown to increase following oral dosing of tryptophan [120].

12. Impairments in a variety of learning and memory skills following tryptophan depletion are well documented [120].

13. In a comparison of adults with and without family histories of bipolar disorder, tryptophan depletion impaired long-term memory consolidation in both groups, and problem-solving was also impaired in those with a family history, while problem-solving improved in those without a family history [120].

14. Tryptophan depletion has also been shown to impair learning on visual discrimination and memory retrieval, episodic memory, stimulus-reward learning, and cognitive flexibility, among other cognitive processes [120].

15. Both animal and human studies have shown that serotonin function is involved in inhibitory control of aggression [120].

16. Tryptophan has been used for a broad spectrum of clinical applications, such as the treatment of pain, insomnia, depression, seasonal affective disorder, bulimia, premenstrual dysphoric disorder, attention-deficit/ hyperactivity disorder, and chronic fatigue [120].

17. Tryptophan has been used for the treatment of sleep disorders and is thought to produce therapeutic effects through melatonin mechanisms [120].

Side effects

Although TRP has been studied for 6 decades, few side effects, which include tremors, nausea, and dizziness, have been reported. A more common effect of high doses of TRP, which can be expected due to the stimulating effect of TRP on serotonin synthesis, is fatigue or drowsiness.

A potentially life-threatening condition is "serotonin syndrome" (also referred to as serotonin toxicity), which includes neuromuscular abnormalities, autonomic hyperactivity, and mental state changes. Serotonin syndrome is usually precipitated by the simultaneous administration of two or more drugs that enhance serotonin availability, such as serotonin reuptake or MAO inhibitors.

In humans, intestinal cells and gut microbiota play an important role in TRP metabolism.

Because TRP is a precursor to serotonin, caution should be exercised when supplementing it with drugs that affect serotonin metabolism [107].

Tryptophan Dosing

Single doses of TRP from 1 g to 15 g were used acutely and chronically for up to 2 years. A commonly used dose is 3 g/day [107]. I started seeing potential contraindicators at more that 2 grams per dose.

L-Citrulline (CIT)

Uses: L-Citrulline can be used instead of L-Arginine because it is synthesized into L-Arginine but without the side effects of taking ARG directly, including an increase in Nitric Oxide. Other benefits of short-term therapy include cardiovascular disorders, muscle wasting, intestinal resection, obesity, and insulin resistance. Unlike all other amino acids listed here, which are sourced primarily from meat, the richest source of CIT is watermelon.

Nitric Oxide: Diminished bioavailability of nitric oxide (NO), the gaseous signaling molecule that regulates numerous vital biological functions, contributes to the development and progression of multiple age and lifestyle-related diseases. Supplementation with l-citrulline has shown promise as a blood pressure lowering intervention (both resting and stress-induced) in adults with pre-/hypertension, with pre-clinical (animal) evidence for atherogenic-endothelial protection. Preliminary evidence is also available for l-citrulline-induced benefits to muscle and metabolic health (via vascular and non-vascular pathways) in susceptible/older populations [128].

Side Effects: Because the main mediators of the effects of CIT supplementation are ARG and NO, and long-term studies of the effect of ARG supplementation indicate cardiovascular and renal risks, studies examining the safety of CIT supplementation are necessary [107].

Dosing: I take 1.5 teaspoons daily.

Amino Acids that Can Be Attained Through Diet

I am primarily a carnivore, so I do not supplement with the following amino acids. However, this is not to say you may not benefit from some of these depending on your objectives and dietary needs.

- **L-Carnitine**
- **Creatine**
- **Glutamine**
- **Leucine**
- **BCAA's**

Why D3, K2, Magnesium, B Complex, and Tryptophan

Must Replace Antidepressants and PTSD Meds

Antidepressants

WARNING: SUICIDAL THOUGHTS AND BEHAVIORS

In October 2004, the FDA required a black box warning for antidepressant drugs of any class that they may increase the risk of suicidality. That warning became effective in January 2005. In 2006, the FDA warning was extended to young adults aged up to 25 years. This is just one of a long list of contraindications, but this is the most significant as it potentially causes what it claims to help.

There is a strong antimicrobial effect of antidepressants from different chemical classes against gut commensal (good) bacteria representative of the predominant species found in the human gut microbiota [35].

As of this writing, the following four antidepressants are used for depression and PTSD in the VA and are widely used in the civilian world. All of these SSRIs will **degrade** beneficial gut bacterial species [35].

- Sertraline (Zoloft)

- Paroxetine (Paxil)

- Fluoxetine (Prozac)

- Venlafaxine (Effexor)

Suicidal thoughts and behaviors are not the only issues with these antidepressants. Following are several more significant contraindicators, but it does not end there. I used Paxil here as an example, but all of the above antidepressants have similar warnings [36].

- **Serotonin Syndrome**: Increased risk when co-administered with other serotonergic agents (e.g., SSRI, SNRI, triptans), but also when taken alone. If this occurs, discontinue PAXIL CR and initiate supportive measures.

- **Embryofetal and Neonatal Toxicity**: Can cause fetal and neonatal harm—increased risk of cardiovascular malformations for exposure during the first trimester. Exposure in late pregnancy may lead to an increased risk of persistent pulmonary hypertension (PPNH) in the newborn.

- **Increased Risk of Bleeding**: Concomitant use of aspirin, nonsteroidal anti-inflammatory drugs, other antiplatelet drugs, warfarin, and other anticoagulant drugs may increase risk.

- **Activation of Mania/Hypomania**: Screen patients for bipolar disorder.

- **Seizures**: Use with caution in patients with seizure disorders.

- **Angle-Closure Glaucoma**: Angle-closure glaucoma has occurred in patients with untreated anatomically narrow angles treated with antidepressants.

- **Sexual Side Effects**: Overall, 73% of SSRI-treated clients reported adverse sexual side effects [36].

- **Weight Gain**: Antidepressants are significantly associated with long-term weight change at two years [37].

Antidepressants and the Placebo Effect

Antidepressants are supposed to work by fixing a chemical imbalance, specifically, a lack of serotonin in the brain. Indeed, their supposed effectiveness is the primary evidence for the chemical imbalance theory. However, analyses of the published and unpublished data that drug companies hid reveal that most (if not all) of the benefits are due to the placebo effect. Some antidepressants increase serotonin levels, some decrease it, and some have no effect at all on serotonin. Nevertheless, they all show the same therapeutic benefit. Even the small statistical difference between antidepressants and placebos may be an enhanced placebo effect due to the fact that most patients and doctors in clinical trials successfully break blind.

The serotonin theory is as close as any theory in science's history to being proved wrong. Instead of curing depression, popular antidepressants may induce a biological vulnerability, making people more likely to become depressed in the future [38]. Does it make sense to use a supplement instead of meds with no side effects and improve your health in multiple ways? If your answer is yes, read on.

D3, K2 (MK-7) Magnesium, B Complex and Tryptophan

Warning: Do not take tryptophan without consulting your physician if you are taking antidepressants.

Vitamin (hormone) D3, K2-7, magnesium, and B Complex work synergistically. K2-7 and magnesium are especially critical when taking high or mega doses of D3. A high dose of D3 is anything up to 100,000 IU. A mega dose of D3 is 100,000 IU and above. I know this sounds like an extraordinary amount, but keep in mind that 40,000 IU of vitamin D is just 1 mg. I will break down all five of these separately, starting with D3.

D3

Anyone who hears about D3 thinks of bone health, but this hormone goes far beyond bone health. Vitamin D receptors (VDR) are found in nearly every cell, and the ability of the cell to produce the active hormone is also widely distributed. Furthermore, the physiological functions with which vitamin D signaling is now associated are as diverse as the tissues in which the vitamin D receptor (VDR) is located [39]. I am going to list just a few attributes of D3 to attempt to drive the point home of how critical D3 is.

1. **All-Cause Mortality**: A meta-analysis of 32 relevant studies found that concentrations less than or equal to 30 ng/mL were associated with higher all-cause mortality than concentrations greater than 30 ng/mL [40].

2. **All-cause, Cardiovascular, Cancer, and Respiratory Disease Mortality**: In this large cohort study, vitamin D deficiency concentration <30 nmol/L] was strongly associated

with mortality from all causes, cardiovascular diseases, cancer, and respiratory diseases [41].

3. **Blood Pressure**: Vitamin D Deficiency Is a Potential Risk for Blood Pressure Elevation and the Development of Hypertension [42].

4. **Depression**: A meta-analysis that included 29 studies with 4,504 participants indicated that the use of vitamin D was beneficial to a decline in the incidence of depression and improvement of depression treatment. Subgroup analysis revealed that people with low vitamin D levels and females could notably benefit from vitamin D in both the prevention and treatment of depression. The effects of vitamin D with a daily supplementary dose of >2,800 IU and intervention duration of ≥8 weeks were considered significant in both prevention and treatment analyses. Intervention duration ≤8 weeks was recognized as effective in the treatment group [44].

5. **Sleep, Pain, and Bowel Symptoms**: Three months of vitamin D plus B100 improved sleep, reduced pain, and unexpectedly resolved bowel symptoms [45]. The reference to B100 in this study was specific to pantothenic acid (B5). The whole foods B Complex I use happens to have 100 mg of B5.

6. **Viruses**: A Systematic Review and Meta-Analysis theoretically established that zero mortality could be achieved from COVID-19 with blood levels of 50 ng/ml or greater [45].

7. **Vitamin D Deficiency Changes the Intestinal Microbiome**: This is the single most significant issue with vitamin D because homeostasis can not occur if the microbiome is not in balance. The combination of vitamin D plus B100 creates an intestinal environment that favors the return of four gut bacterial species, **Actinobacteria**, **Bacteroidetes**, **Firmicutes**, and **Proteobacteria**, that comprise the normal human microbiome [45].

These bacteria represent the majority of friendly bacteria in the gut, with Firmicutes and Bacteroidetes representing 90% of gut microbiota [46].

D3 Blood Levels

The recommendations for vitamin D blood levels are all over the map. Low is considered <20 ng/ml, with 30 to 60 in the normal range. I consider 50 ng/ml to be the minimum, with a goal range of 70 to 90 ng/ml. This is because a Systematic Review and Meta-Analysis theoretically established that zero mortality could be achieved from COVID-19 with 50 ng/ml [45]. If 50 ng/ml of vitamin D will save your life from the next pandemic, it simply makes sense to look at that as the minimum, NOT 30 ng/ml.

D3 Dosing

The current D3 dosing recommendation from NIH is 600 IU for people between the ages of 1 and 70 [41]. This is one of the biggest lies in the medical community. This amount was established in the 1930s to prevent rickets in children and is woefully inadequate for multiple other issues and most people, including children. The Endocrine Society has recently increased its recommended amount of D3, but I believe an acceptable range should be established instead of making up an ultra-conservative number to try and conform to 100% of the population. My position on this is based on the following data.

- Vitamin D can be produced in the skin in amounts estimated up to 25,000 international units (IUs) a day by the action of UVB radiation [47].

- In a hospital setting, 4,700 patients admitted over seven years were administered 5000 to 50,000 IU of D3 per day without any sign of Hypervitaminosis, Hypercalcemia, or any adverse events attributable to vitamin D3 supplementation in any patient [47].

D3 Hypervitaminosis and Hypercalcemia

Getting poisoned from vitamin D3 is extremely rare. I only found one case and a relative reported the amount and timeline it was taken [48]. The big concern with taking too much D3 is hypercalcemia, which is too much calcium in the blood, enabling it to accumulate in the arteries. This can be circumvented with vitamin K2-7, which is why I believe one should always take K2 with D3.

Vitamin K2-7

Clinical studies have unequivocally demonstrated the utility of vitamin K2-7 supplementation in ameliorating peripheral neuropathy, reducing bone fracture risk, and improving cardiovascular health. K2-7 accomplishes this with the protein synthesis of osteocalcin and various other proteins [49]. This means that K2-7 delivers calcium where it is supposed to go.

Vitamin K2-7 and Vascular Calcification

Vascular calcification is characterized by mineral depositions on the walls of the vascular system. This is the primary concern when taking high or mega doses of D3. K2 has the potential to inhibit as well as reverse the process of calcification [50]. The benefits of K2 do not stop at simply delivering calcium where it is supposed to go and freeing calcium present in the blood vessels.

- Vitamin K2 suppresses cancer cell growth via apoptosis, autophagy, and cell-cycle arrest [50]

- Vitamin K2 improves sensitivity to insulin in diabetic patients [50]

- Vitamin K2 facilitates the synthesis and repair of the myelin sheath in the peripheral nervous system [50]

- Vitamin K2 has the potential to slow down the progression of Alzheimer's Disease and contribute to its prevention [50]

Contraindications to Vitamin K2-7

There are no severe adverse effects due to the supplementation of vitamin K2-7. However, high doses of vitamin K2 can cause allergic reactions [50].

Sources of K2-7

Sources of K2-7 include natto, which is the highest, moderate in chicken, sauerkraut, beef, and a variety of cheeses, and is low in pork, salmon, etc. [50].

K2 Dosing

I do not go beyond the dose that is part of the D3 K2 supplement that I take.

Magnesium

Magnesium assists in activating vitamin D, which helps regulate calcium and phosphate homeostasis to influence the growth and maintenance of bones.

All enzymes that metabolize vitamin D seem to require magnesium, which acts as a cofactor in the enzymatic reactions in the liver and kidneys [26]. This is why you can become deficient in magnesium if high doses of D3 are taken, even if you are taking the daily RDA. As one increases, D3 magnesium must also be increased.

B Complex

As mentioned above, three months of B100 or B5 (pantothenic acid) and vitamin D improved sleep, reduced pain, and unexpected resolution of bowel symptoms [45].

This combination also creates an intestinal environment that favors the return of four foundational gut bacterial species, Actinobacteria, Bacteroidetes, Firmicutes, and Proteobacteria, that make up the normal human microbiome [45] before and after comprehensive stool tests prove this to be accurate.

Tryptophan

SSRIs do not make new serotonin, but tryptophan does, along with melatonin and NAD, and this is why it is added to this stack again; consult with your MD before taking tryptophan if you are taking antidepressants.

Kelly Burris: <u>Comprehensive Stool Test: 9-20</u>

If you look under **Commensal Microbiome Analysis**, you will see the four foundational bacteria and a couple of others. All were low, with Euryarchaeota Phylum below detectable levels. MDs, nutritionists, and even Functional Medicine Practitioners recommended probiotics, so I took their advice and researched the top probiotics, taking up to 1.7 trillion CFUs daily. As you can see, it had little to no effect on the commensal bacteria. This is not to say that probiotics do not work because taking the right ones can be very effective. Just do not depend on them to reestablish foundational commensal bacteria.

Kelly Burris: <u>Comprehensive Stool Test: 9-22</u>

Seven weeks before doing this test, I did high doses of vitamin D with 12 days of mega-dosing, which I do not recommend. I was already taking a B Complex that included 100 mg of B5. Another interesting piece is that plant-based diets are recommended to increase Firmicutes Phylum. I had been primarily a carnivore for 33 months when this test was done, yet there were significant increases in all commensal (good) bacteria. Another thing to look at with these two tests is "The Need for Microbiome Support" at the top of the page. Part of this equation is yeast overgrowth (Candida), and this test completely missed it as I was still a 10, as the first one indicated. All tests I had for yeast overgrowth were unreliable. This is after 3 comprehensive tests, 2 standard tests, and several urine tests.

Additional Attributes Of B Complex

B1 (Thiamin and Benfotiamine)

Severe alcoholism can be associated with significant nutritional and vitamin deficiency, especially vitamin B1 (thiamine), associated with neurological deficits impacting mood and cognition. Benfotiamine appears to reduce psychiatric distress and may facilitate recovery in severely affected males with a lifetime alcohol use disorder [142]. I used Benfotiamine to cure my neuromyelitis optica.

Individuals with thiamin deficiency also require other nutrient supplementation, such as magnesium, vitamin B2 (riboflavin), B3 (nicotinamide), B6 (pyridoxine), B12, vitamin C, potassium, and phosphate. Taking a good B Complex, in my opinion, is the best way to go.

Toxicity

The human body excretes excess thiamin in the urine. There is a lack of evidence of toxicity from high thiamin intake from food or supplements. Food and Nutrition Board (FNB) concluded that excessive consumption of thiamin might cause adverse effects despite a lack of substantial evidence of toxicity. Per the Institute of Medicine, no established upper limit of thiamin intake is reported in the literature to cause any toxicity [63].

B2 (Riboflavin): B2 can be found in a wide variety of foods and natural sources, especially milk and organ meats, mostly in calf liver, egg, fish, nuts, certain fruits and legumes, wild rice, mushrooms, dark green leafy vegetables, yeast, beer, cheese, and dietary products.

Vertebrates poorly store B2 because of its limited absorption in humans. Therefore, orally supplied RF by a healthy diet is required to avoid ariboflavinosis, which causes cheilitis, sore tongue, and a scaly rash on the scrotum or vulva. B2 causes no known toxicity since it is excreted in the urine at higher intakes and not stored. B2 is found in different concentrations in various human body fluids and organs [52].

- B2 reduces reactive oxygen species
- B2 was used for its potent antioxidant and anti-inflammatory effects

- B2 plays an important role in the antioxidant status inside cell systems and is part of the glutathione reductase
- B2 functions as an endogenous antioxidant in different cells
- B2 can attenuate oxidative injuries through its ability to scavenge free radicals and, therefore, decrease re-oxygenation injuries
- B2 is neuroprotective of cerebral ischemia
- B2 intake from food sources was associated with a decrease in the risk of PMS
- B2 with co-treatment with selenium or vitamin E can protect the brain and microsomal membrane.
- B2 contributes to blood cell formation
- B2 was shown to enhance iron absorption

B3 (Niacin): B3 includes two vitamers (nicotinic acid and nicotinamide), giving rise to the coenzymatic forms nicotinamide adenine dinucleotide (NAD+). The two coenzymes are required for oxidative reactions crucial for energy production, but they are also substrates for enzymes involved in non-redox signaling pathways, thus regulating biological functions, including gene expression, cell cycle progression, DNA repair, and cell death. Vitamin B3 has long been recognized as a key mediator of neuronal development and survival in the central nervous system.

Humans obtain niacin from both endogenous and exogenous sources. Only 2% of dietary tryptophan is converted into niacin via a multistep pathway, occurring mainly in the liver. Diet provides vitamins such as nicotinic acid, nicotinamide, and tryptophan, as well as the active coenzymatic forms of niacin. Niacin is found in animal and vegetable foods. In meat and fish, the vitamin is present as nicotinamide, whose amounts are higher in unprepared foods compared to processed foods.

Severe niacin and/or tryptophan deficiency leads to a variety of clinical symptoms, including diarrhea, dermatitis, and dementia, collectively known as "pellagra." Pellagra is common in people who mostly eat maize, as well as in malnourished and alcoholic men. Other risk factors leading to vitamin B3 deficiency are nervous anorexia, AIDS, cancer, and malabsorptive disorders, such as Crohn's disease [53].

Toxicity

Niacin-associated hepatotoxicity is generally related to ingestions of around 3 grams per day. In contrast, the more common symptom of flushing can occur at doses as low as 30 mg per day [54]. The flushing was significant when I took just 250 mg of nicotinic acid on an empty stomach. No flushing occurred at 250 mg after eating.

B5 (Pantothenic Acid): Vitamin B5 is a naturally occurring substance in various plants and animals (i.e., eggs, milk, vegetables, beef, chicken).

An experimental vitamin B5 deficiency study associated the deficiency with symptoms such as fatigue, headache, malaise, personality changes, numbness, muscle cramps, paresthesia, muscle/ abdominal cramps, nausea, and impaired muscle coordination [55].

Toxicity

B5 is considered generally safe. There are currently no upper limits established since there have been no reports of vitamin B5 toxicity in humans with high intakes. However, there are still side effects involved with B5 administration [55].

B6 (Pyridoxine): B6 is involved in the vast majority of changes in the human body because it is a coenzyme involved in over 150 biochemical reactions. It is active in metabolizing carbohydrates, lipids, amino acids, and nucleic acids and participates in cellular signaling. In addition, it is an antioxidant and a compound that can lower the advanced glycation end products (AGE) level [56].

Pyridoxal 5' phosphate (P-5-P) is the active coenzyme form of vitamin B6. P-5-P deficiency leads to immunosuppression, local exacerbation of inflammatory processes, and increased secretion of proinflammatory cytokines. Conversely, replenishing P-5-P may boost immunity and maintain an equilibrium that allows control of viral replication without uncontrolled expression of cytokines [56]. At the time of my first NutrVal test, I was taking 50 mg of B6 in the form of P-5-P per day, and I was deficient. This is a good example of why you always want to test, not guess, because 50 mg should have been more than adequate, but the variable of oxalate poisoning and a disrupted microbiota significantly increased my requirement for B6.

Toxicity

Most studies indicate that an intake below 200 mg of pyridoxine daily does not cause issues [56]. I am taking 225 mg daily of P-5-P.

Warning: Avoid Pyridoxine HCL as it can cause peripheral neuropathy in therapeutic amounts instead of helping peripheral neuropathy [146]. Some MDs do not distinguish between P-5-P and pyridoxine HCL, which is a mistake.

B7 (Biotin): Marginal and severe degrees of biotin deficiency lead to various clinical abnormalities, including neurological disorders and dermal abnormalities. Such deficiency/suboptimal levels occur in a variety of conditions, including inflammatory bowel disease (IBD). At the metabolic level, biotin acts as a cofactor for five carboxylases that are critical for fatty acid, glucose, and amino acid metabolism. Essential roles for this vitamin in cellular energy metabolism (i.e., ATP production) and in the regulation of cellular oxidative stress (24), as well as in gene expression where expression of over 2,000 human genes appears to be affected by biotin status, have also been reported recently. An increase in the levels of proinflammatory cytokines has also been observed in biotin deficiency [57].

Toxicity

Although not impossible, it would be very difficult to overdose on biotin.

Since biotin has been documented to play a role in postprandial glucose control, it bears mention that excess would cause signs and symptoms of a person experiencing hyperglycemia (e.g., increased thirst). Diabetic patients should, therefore, be cautious before taking biotin [58].

B9 (Folate): The decreased folate level of the body, mainly caused by environmental and hereditary factors as well as aging, can lead to genetic, epigenetic, and metabolic changes. It can be related to the development of megaloblastic anemia, various cardiovascular diseases (such as atherosclerosis and stroke), obstetrical complications (such as abruption of the placentae, spontaneous abortion, preterm delivery, neural tube defect), neuropsychiatric diseases (such as Alzheimer's disease, Parkinson's disease, depression) and tumors [59].

Toxicity

Recent folate intervention trials suggest that folate supplementation may increase the risk of the above chronic diseases for individuals at a higher risk [60]. This is why folate does not exceed 200% of the daily value.

B12 (Cobalamin): B12 is a cofactor for enzymes involved in synthesizing deoxyribonucleic acid (DNA), fatty acids, and myelin. B12 deficiency can lead to hematologic and neurological symptoms. Vitamin B12 is stored in excess in the liver, decreasing the likelihood of deficiency. However, hepatic stores are depleted in cases where vitamin B12 cannot be absorbed, such as dietary insufficiency, malabsorption, or lack of intrinsic factor, and deficiency ensues [61-62-63].

Sources of B12 are animal products such as red meat, dairy, and eggs.

Toxicity

No toxic effects of vitamin B-12 have been identified, even when it is administered intramuscularly at 300–3000 times the recommended dietary allowance. For this reason, no upper tolerable level for the vitamin has been established [62].

B12: Which Type to Take

Methylcobalamin is the recommended B12.

Avoid cyanocobalamin.

Probiotics

Probiotics are the wild wild west of supplements. There is virtually no regulation of probiotics, making it difficult to know which ones to take, for what, and how much of each strain is in a probiotic. After extensive research on probiotics, I established what I call the essential 7. The task was then to find a probiotic that contained these bacteria.

Recommended Probiotic

Dr. Formulated Once Daily Women's 50 Billion CFU: It has a balance of 40 billion lacto cultures and 10 billion bifido cultures and contains the essential 7 probiotics listed below.

Essential Probiotic 7

1. Lactobacillus Reuteri

- L. Reuteri significantly reduces chronic functional abdominal pain in children [64.]

- High-fat-diet-induced obesity is associated with decreased anti-inflammatory L. Reuteri [65].

- L. Reuteri reduces hepatic cancer cell proliferation, muscle wasting, and morbidity and prolongs survival [66].

- L. Reuteri attenuates stressor-enhanced infectious Colitis [67].

2.Lactobacillus Rhamnosus

- L. Rhamnosus provides protective effects on alcoholic liver injury by reducing oxidative stress and restoring the intestinal flora [68].

- L. Rhamnosus diminishes oxidative markers in the brain [69].

- L. Rhamnosus protects against tissue damage mediated through free radicals and inflammatory cytokines [70].

3.Lactobacillus Acidophilus

- L. Acidophilus restrains the development of S. aureus and P. aeruginosa enteric infections [71].

- Exopolysaccharides (EPS) from Lactobacillus acidophilus have antioxidative properties [72].

- Surface layer protein A (SlpA) from Lactobacillus acidophilus NCFM potentially represents a feasible therapeutic approach to restore intestinal homeostasis [73].

4.Lactobacillus Plantarum

- L. Plantarum potentially enhances the immunity of the small intestine [74]

- L. Plantarum could ameliorate anxiety and depression-like behaviors and modulate neurochemicals related to affective disorders [75].

- L. Plantarum positively affects the immune system and acts as an antiviral [76].

5.Lactobacillus Brevis

- L. Brevis synthesizes gamma-aminobutyric acid (GABA) [77]. GABA is the most potent depressive neuroamine in human brains. It regulates many of the depressive and sedative actions in brain tissue and is critical to relaxation [78].

- L. Brevis may prevent some metabolic disturbances [79].

6. Bifidobacterium Lactis

- B. Lactis improves the intestinal microbiota more effectively than non-proliferating bifidobacteria and lactic acid bacteria [80].

- B. Lactis improves defecation frequency [81].

- As part of a multispecies probiotic blend, B. lactis showed cognitive reactivity to sad mood, which was largely accounted for by reduced rumination and aggressive thoughts [82].

7. Bifidobacterium Longum

- B. Longum decreases the excitability of enteric (gut) neurons [83].

- B. Longum has anti-allergy effects, reducing harmful bacteria, improving intestinal environment, defecation frequency, and improved stool characteristics [84].

- B. Longum supplementation prevents bone loss and increases bone formation [85].

Probiotic Administration

The majority of human gut microbiota is present in the large intestine. This makes it difficult to repopulate with probiotics. Dr. Perlmutter has solved this issue by recommending probiotic enemas.

As he clearly stated in his book, do not do this without permission from your MD or functional medicine practitioner. Tourette syndrome was just one of the disorders he cured using this method. The Tourette syndrome enema contained 1.2 trillion CFUs.

Kefir Raw Cheese and Bulgarian Yogurt

Kefir is associated with a wide array of nutraceutical benefits, including anti-inflammatory, anti-oxidative, anti-cancer, anti-microbial, anti-diabetic, anti-hypertensive, and anti-hypercholesterolemic effects [155]. I also noticed a difference in getting kefir made with A2 milk as opposed to A1. I also noticed kefir can cause weight gain around the middle if used in excess.

Raw Cheese: Lactic acid bacteria (LAB) play an essential role in traditional cheese making, either as starter cultures that cause the rapid acidification of milk or as secondary microbiota that play an important role during cheese ripening. Several studies in animal models have unfolded the therapeutic effect associated with the administration of probiotic LAB strains upon cognitive processes and a reduction in psychophysiological markers of anxiety and depression. Current scientific evidence suggests that LAB, mainly Lactobacillus and Bifidobacterium, are beneficial to the host in correcting imbalances in the intestinal microbiota and consequently in maintaining and regulating health [156].

Bulgarian Yogurt: Bulgarian yogurt is a rich source of strains producing exopolysaccharides (EPS), macromolecular compounds known for their anticancer and immunomodulatory activity, as well as the ability to maintain the intestinal barrier by regulating the functions of the gut microbiome [161]. While most other yogurts measure their CFUs in the millions, White Mountain Bulgarian Yogurt claims upward of 90 billion CFUs per cup.0

The Inflammatory 9

1. **Anti-Nutrients and Plant Toxins**: This includes oxidants, lectins, goitrogens, phytoestrogens, phytolates, and tannins. Grains, in particular, can also alter the composition of gut microbiota [87].

2. **High IgG4 Food Antigens**: If over-stimulation of IgG4 is an issue, symptom improvement is confirmed by eliminating beef, pork, lamb, egg whites, and wheat.

3. **FODMAPs:** The acronym FODMAPs (fermentable oligosaccharides, disaccharides, monosaccharides, and polyols) describes poorly absorbed, short-chain carbohydrates [157].

4. **Alcohol and Sugar**:
   - Alcohol increases intestinal permeability by disrupting the microbiota [86].
   - The dysbiosis caused by alcohol can perpetuate the habit of drinking [86].
   - Alcohol use can lead to more than 200 disorders, including hypertension [149].
   - Alcohol makes mitochondria more vulnerable to oxidative damage, which precedes dysfunction [150].
   - Brain mitochondria appear to be the principal targets of the oxidative stress generated by ethanol intoxication and withdrawal [150].
   - Refined and artificial sugars alter the gut microbiota composition [87]. I included sugar here because I refer to alcohol as liquid sugar.

5. **NSAIDs**: Nonsteroidal anti-inflammatory drugs include aspirin, ibuprofen, and naproxen. These drugs are linked to the onset of IBD [88].

6. **Milk Fat**: MF increases the presence of Bilophila Wadsworth, which is a gut bacteria associated with IBD and Colitis [148]. Kefir and raw organic grass-fed cheddar are exempt.
   Likewise, Ghee is exempt as it is free of lactose, casein, and whey. Because of butyrate in butter, it is also exempt.

7. **Some Polyunsaturated Fats**: Certain PUFAs disrupt the balance of the gut microbiota [89].

8. **Preservatives**: I discovered this one inadvertently while researching Candida antimicrobials. The nearly universal antimicrobial activity attributed to grapefruit seed extract is merely due to the synthetic preservative agents contained within.
   Natural products with antimicrobial activity do not appear to be present [90]. The assumption based on this research is that preservatives act as an antimicrobial. If one takes an antibiotic or antimicrobial, they must be accompanied by probiotics to assist

in preventing dysbiosis, but I am certain very few people know that preventives act as an antimicrobial.

9. **Caffeine**: Cortisol [91] is a stress hormone, and caffeine can cause a robust increase in cortisol [92]. I know how hard it is to quit caffeine, and coffee has many benefits. There should, however, be a consideration of switching to decaf until the dysbiosis is under control.

CBD: Reduce Nausea, Improve Sleep, and Lower Toxicity, Inflammation, and Pathogens

CBD (cannabidiol) is the non-psychoactive component of cannabis. With over two thousand full-text articles on PMC, I came to find that CBD had more uses than just as an antipathogen [95]. It was the most industrial-grade anti-inflammatory I had ever used [96].

Studies on models of human diseases support the idea that CBD attenuates inflammation far beyond its antioxidant properties by targeting inflammation-related intracellular signaling events. The details on how it does this remain to be defined.

The use of THC and Candida in a mouse model was deemed ineffective [93]. However, Candida colonization delays the healing of inflammatory lesions, and inflammation promotes colonization. These effects may create a vicious cycle in which low-level inflammation promotes fungal colonization, and fungal colonization promotes further inflammation. High-level Candida colonization is frequently observed in ulcer and IBD patients and is linked to Crohn's disease, ulcerative Colitis, and leaky gut [34]. During this vicious cycle, the profound anti-inflammatory processes of CBD became very useful in eradicating pathogenetic candida.

Because cannabinoids are profoundly anti-inflammatory, infections caused by HIV-1 or HSV-1 can worsen. The anti-inflammatory action can impair dependent enzyme systems which are central to inflammatory and cell-autonomous antiviral responses [94]. This was not the case with me, so the industrial-grade anti-inflammatory nature of CBD worked very well.

Getting Started with CBD

Warning: Even though CBD is difficult to overdose on, it seems good at killing yeast and removing pathogens, making starting with high doses relatively dangerous.

The only way to take CBD is in the purest form possible. This is in the form of CBD oil combined with coconut or MCT oil. Some CBD sprays contain Polysorbate 80. Polysorbate 80 is linked to low-grade intestinal inflammation and metabolic syndrome—a group of conditions that increase the risk for type 2 diabetes, heart disease, and stroke.[247] Always ensure that you are taking only oil and CBD.

For me, CBD was an important factor in getting through the extreme toxicity brought on by fasting and therapeutic amounts of olive oil.

Where to Purchase CBD

I get mine at CBD Market because I don't particularly appreciate digging for coupons; they have the best prices.

Mitochondrial Regeneration: The Key to Energy, Health Span, and Longevity

Mitochondria are engaged in the pathogenesis of human diseases and aging directly or indirectly through a broad range of signaling pathways. They are the cell's primary source of ATP (Adenosine triphosphate) and play a pivotal role in cell life and death. ATP is the energy source for use and storage at the cellular level [97]. This is why most in the medical community refer to the mitochondria as the cell's powerhouse.

Due to their central role in cell life and death, mitochondria are also involved in the pathogenesis and progression of numerous human diseases, including, among others, cancer, neurodegenerative and cardiovascular disorders, diabetes, traumatic brain injury, and inflammation [97].

Mitochondria and Emotional Fitness (Mental Health)

The mitochondrial response to stress is communicated both locally within the cell and systemically throughout the body. Exposure to stress mediators precipitates the mitochondrial release of signaling molecules, collectively called mitokines. Mitokines serve as signals that indicate mitochondrial fitness, which is particularly important in environmental stressors. Mitokines include various mitochondrial metabolites, calcium, and reactive oxygen species (ROS). When elevated, ROS overwhelms the cell's antioxidant capacity and promotes oxidative stress, causing cell death and tissue damage. These mechanisms allow mitochondria to influence broad physiological processes throughout the body, including molecular mechanisms of aging and stress-related conditions, psychiatric disorders, cardiovascular disease, obesity, diabetes, and cancer [145].

If you view your body as an electric vehicle, the batteries would be the mitochondria. Unfortunately, over time, the batteries become dysfunctional and slowly die while your energy slows down until the entire machine dies unless there is consistent maintenance and replacement of the dysfunctional cells. I know this is an oversimplification, but the important thing is to understand the impact and importance of mitochondria. Maintenance and replacement of the mitochondria is a multipronged approach that includes diet, exercise, and supplementation, which we will discuss below.

If you would like to go full geek on mitochondria, especially in terms of the brain and human behavior, you may want to look at a book called Brain Energy. I am not in agreement with this author's assertion that the mitochondria are at the root of mental illness, but he is at least headed in a good direction.

Mitochondria Supplement Stack

PQQ (Pyrroloquinoline Quinone): PQQ is associated with biological processes such as mitochondriogenesis, reproduction, growth, and aging. In addition, PQQ attenuates clinically relevant dysfunctions (e.g., those associated with ischemia, inflammation, and lipotoxicity) [98]. This is the only supplement I am aware of that regrows new mitochondria.

Niacin: Niacin (vitamin B3) comes in three forms, nicotinamide, niaciniamide and nicotinic acid. Nicotinic acid causes flushing, while nicotinamide and niacinamide do not. They all increase NAD+ (nicotinamide adenine dinucleotide) in higher amounts, while nicotinic acid improves your lipid profile, but nicotinamide and niacinamide do not [129].

Niacin modulates Sert 1 (serotonin transporter), [131] which promoters of NMN use to market their product; however, they will state that niacin suppresses Sert 1 when the medical literature clearly states that it modulates it. To be clear, the modulation of Sert 1 by niacin is how nicotinic acid inhibits vascular inflammation [132].

NAD+: Nicotinamide adenine dinucleotide (NAD+) is an important coenzyme for redox reactions (electron transport and transfer), making it central to energy metabolism.

The slow, inevitable aging process has been described as a "cascade of robustness breakdown triggered by a decrease in systemic NAD+ biosynthesis and the resultant functional defects in susceptible organs and tissues [124]. Niacin is an efficient NAD+ booster for treating mitochondrial myopathy [139]. In this study, 750 to 1000 mg was used for 4 and 10 months, but I have looked at individual data that showed improvements in NAD+ with much less using nicotinic acid. I take 500 mg of nicotinic acid after eating. Taking it on an empty stomach can cause significant flushing. This is another vitamin that you will want to start slowly. I am currently using niacinamide.

NMN and NR (Nicotinamide Mononucleotide and Nicotinamide Riboside): NMN and NR are forms of vitamin B3 and a precursor to NAD+. I do not recommend or use either of these versions of B3.

By middle age, our NAD+ levels have plummeted to half that of our youth. Numerous studies have demonstrated that boosting NAD+ levels increases insulin sensitivity, reverses mitochondrial dysfunction, and extends lifespan. NAD+ levels can be increased by activating enzymes that stimulate the synthesis of NAD+, by inhibiting an enzyme (CD38) that degrades NAD+, and by supplementing with NAD precursors, including niacin and NMN [124].

Luteolin: CD38 is an enzyme that increases with age via inflammation, and this decreases NAD+. This inflammation is induced by senescent cells (dying cells.) Luteolin and other supplements, such as apigenin, suppress CD38 [133]. This is why autophagy may be even more important as we age because the body consumes senescent cells when in an autophagic state, which, in theory, should also help to lower CD38. I say in theory because there are no studies on this subject at this time.

Urolithin A: Urolithin A (UA) is produced by gut microflora from foods rich in ellagitannins. UA has been shown to improve mitochondrial health preclinically and in humans. Not everyone has a microbiome capable of producing UA, making supplementation with UA an appealing strategy [158]. Urolithin A has been shown to promote mitophagy (clearance of dysfunctional mitochondria), mitochondrial function, and improved muscle function across species in different experimental models and across multiple clinical studies [159]. One cause of the loss of mitochondrial homeostasis during aging is the accumulation of dysfunctional mitochondria [159]. Fasting and exercise also induce mitophagy. Mitophagy must occur to enable mitochondrial biogenesis (generation of new mitochondria).

AKG (Alpha-Ketoglutarate): Recent studies in experimental models have shown that dietary AKG reduces reactive oxygen species (ROS) production and systemic inflammatory cytokine levels, regulates metabolism, extends lifespan, and delays the occurrence of age-related decline [122]. Mechanistically, AKG leads to an energetic state that is reprogrammed toward a mitochondrial metabolism, with increased oxidative phosphorylation and expression of complex mitochondrial enzymes [123].

ALA (R-Alpha Lipoic Acid): The R in Alpha Lipoic Acid indicates it is the natural, more bioavailable form. This supplement must be taken on an empty stomach for maximum bioavailability. ALA is synthesized in the mitochondria and plays an essential role as a cofactor, assisting in the enzymatic nutrient breakdown.

ALA is considered generally safe. A daily dose of 200 to 2400 mg/day of ALA is deemed safe without side effects. However, there is no reported safety dose in children [125]. The max I take is 600 mg a day on an empty stomach.

CoQ10 (Coenzyme Q10): In addition to shuttling electrons in the mitochondrial respiratory chain, CoQ10 serves several additional cellular functions, including the transfer of electrons in plasma membranes and lysosomes, modulation of apoptosis (cell death) proton transport of uncoupling proteins, and antioxidant activity including inhibition of lipid peroxidation [134]. My numbers were good for CoQ10, so I do not supplement, but if I did supplement, I would use the freeze-dried beef heart capsules.

L Carnitine

L-carnitine is one of the key nutrients for proper mitochondrial function and is notable for its role in fatty acid oxidation.

L-carnitine also plays a major part in protecting cellular membranes, preventing fatty acid accumulation, modulating ketogenesis and glucogenesis, and in the elimination of toxic metabolites. L-carnitine deficiency has been observed in many diseases, including organic acidurias, inborn errors of metabolism, endocrine imbalances, and liver and kidney disease [126]. I do not supplement with l-carnitine.

Creatine

Creatine monohydrate (CrM) is one of the most widely used nutritional supplements among active individuals and athletes to improve high-intensity exercise performance and training adaptations. However, research suggests that CrM supplementation may also serve as a therapeutic tool in the management of some chronic and traumatic diseases. Creatine supplementation has been reported to improve high-energy phosphate availability as well as have antioxidative, neuroprotective, anti-lactic, and calcium-homoeostatic effects. These characteristics may directly impact mitochondrion survival and health, particularly during stressful conditions such as ischemia and injury [135]. I do not supplement with creatine.

Omega 3 Fatty Acids

Mitochondrial dysfunction represents a common early pathological event in brain aging and in neurodegenerative diseases, e.g., Alzheimer's (AD), Parkinson's (PD), and Huntington's disease (HD), as well as in ischemic stroke. In vivo and ex vivo experiments using animal models of aging and AD, PD, and HD mainly showed improvement in mitochondrial function after treatment with polyunsaturated fatty acids (PUFA), such as docosahexaenoic acid (DHA) [136]. My test showed low omega 3, so I supplement with Total Omega 3 Full Spectrum by Sports Research.

B Complex

Mitochondria are compromised by a deficiency of any B vitamin [137]. More details on this are in the B vitamin section of this paper.

Vitamin D

Skeletal muscle mitochondrial function is the biggest component of whole-body energy output. Mitochondrial energy production during exercise is impaired in vitamin D-deficient subjects. Vitamin D supplementation initiated in older people improved muscle mass and strength [138].

Vitamin C

Vitamin C quenches mitochondrial ROS (reactive oxygen species) and inhibits oxidative mitochondrial DNA damage [141].

Minerals

Mitochondria are particularly rich in minerals, where they function as essential cofactors for mitochondrial physiology and overall cellular health. Eleven of the 12 minerals essential for human health have important roles within mitochondrial metabolism. However, this picture is not yet complete [140]. The bottom line is to make sure that all minerals are well-balanced.

The Sleep Stack

Tryptophan

Vitamin D

Luteolin

Magnesium

Glycine

CBD

I use tryptophan, vitamin D, and luteolin an hour before bed. It takes experimentation to find what works.

References

1. Umar S. Intestinal stem cells. Curr Gastroenterol Rep. 2010 Oct;12(5):340-8. doi: 10.1007/s11894-010-0130-3. PMID: 20683682; PMCID: PMC2965634.

2. Sánchez de Medina F, Romero-Calvo I, Mascaraque C, Martínez-Augustin O. Intestinal inflammation and mucosal barrier function. Inflamm Bowel Dis. 2014 Dec;20(12):2394-404. doi: 10.1097/MIB.0000000000000204. PMID: 25222662.

3. Brittan M, Wright NA. Stem cell in gastrointestinal structure and neoplastic development. Gut. 2004 Jun;53(6):899-910. doi: 10.1136/gut.2003.025478. PMID: 15138220; PMCID: PMC1774081.

4. Galve-Roperh I, Chiurchiù V, Díaz-Alonso J, Bari M, Guzmán M, Maccarrone M. Cannabinoid receptor signaling in progenitor/stem cell proliferation and differentiation. Prog Lipid Res. 2013 Oct;52(4):633-50. doi: 10.1016/j.plipres.2013.05.004. Epub 2013 Sep 25. PMID: 24076098.

5. Brosnan ME, Brosnan JT. Histidine Metabolism and Function. J Nutr. 2020 Oct 1;150(Suppl 1):2570S-2575S. doi: 10.1093/jn/nxaa079. PMID: 33000155; PMCID: PMC7527268.

6. Wollersen H, Erdmann F, Risse M, Dettmeyer R. Oxalate-crystals in different tissues following intoxication with ethylene glycol: three case reports. Leg Med (Tokyo). 2009 Apr;11 Suppl 1:S488-90. doi: 10.1016/j.legalmed.2009.01.098. Epub 2009 Feb 28. PMID: 19251453.

7. Chutipongtanate S, Sutthimethakorn S, Chiangjong W, Thongboonkerd V. Bacteria can promote calcium oxalate crystal growth and aggregation. J Biol Inorg Chem. 2013 Mar;18(3):299-308. doi: 10.1007/s00775-012-0974-0. Epub 2013 Jan 20. Erratum in: J Biol Inorg Chem. 2013 Apr;18(4):485-6. PMID: 23334195.

8. Klaerner HG, Uknis ME, Acton RD, Dahlberg PS, Carlone-Jambor C, Dunn DL. Candida albicans and Escherichia coli are synergistic pathogens during experimental microbial peritonitis. J Surg Res. 1997 Jul 1;70(2):161-5. doi: 10.1006/jsre.1997.5110. PMID: 9245566.

9. Suryavanshi MV, Bhute SS, Jadhav SD, Bhatia MS, Gune RP, Shouche YS. Hyperoxaluria leads to dysbiosis and drives selective enrichment of oxalate metabolizing bacterial species in recurrent kidney stone endures. Sci Rep. 2016 Oct 6;6:34712. doi: 10.1038/srep34712. PMID: 27708409; PMCID: PMC5052600.

10. Lorenz EC, Michet CJ, Milliner DS, Lieske JC. Update on oxalate crystal disease. Curr Rheumatol Rep. 2013 Jul;15(7):340. doi: 10.1007/s11926-013-0340-4. PMID: 23666469; PMCID: PMC3710657.

11. Zampini A, Nguyen AH, Rose E, Monga M, Miller AW. Defining Dysbiosis in Patients with Urolithiasis. Sci Rep. 2019 Apr 1;9(1):5425. doi: 10.1038/s41598-019-41977-6. PMID: 30932002; PMCID: PMC6443657.

12. Liebman M, Al-Wahsh IA. Probiotics and other key determinants of dietary oxalate absorption. Adv Nutr. 2011 May;2(3):254-60. doi: 10.3945/an.111.000414. Epub 2011 Apr 30. PMID: 22332057; PMCID: PMC3090165.

13. Miles MR, Olsen L, Rogers A. Recurrent vaginal candidiasis. Importance of an intestinal reservoir. JAMA. 1977 Oct 24;238(17):1836-7. doi: 10.1001/jama.238.17.1836. PMID: 333134.

14. Omar SH. Oleuropein in olive and its pharmacological effects. Sci Pharm. 2010 Apr-Jun;78(2):133-54. doi: 10.3797/scipharm.0912-18. Epub 2010 Apr 23. PMID: 21179340; PMCID: PMC3002804.

15. Segura-Carretero A, Curiel JA. Current Disease-Targets for Oleocanthal as Promising Natural Therapeutic Agent. Int J Mol Sci. 2018 Sep 24;19(10):2899. doi: 10.3390/ijms19102899. PMID: 30250008; PMCID: PMC6213726.

16. Peyrol J, Riva C, Amiot MJ. Hydroxytyrosol in the Prevention of the Metabolic Syndrome and Related Disorders. Nutrients. 2017 Mar 20;9(3):306. doi: 10.3390/nu9030306. PMID: 28335507; PMCID: PMC5372969.

17. Nasrolla7hi Z, Abolhasannezhad M. Evaluation of the antifungal activity of olive leaf aqueous extracts against Candida albicans PTCC-5027. Curr Med Mycol. 2015 Dec;1(4):37-39. doi: 10.18869/acadpub.cmm.1.4.37. PMID: 28681003; PMCID: PMC5490280.

18. Yadav M, Jain S, Tomar R, Prasad GB, Yadav H. Medicinal and biological potential of pumpkin: an updated review. Nutr Res Rev. 2010 Dec;23(2):184-90. doi: 10.1017/S0954422410000107. PMID: 21110905.

19. Goel N, Rohilla H, Singh G, Punia P. Antifungal Activity of Cinnamon Oil and Olive Oil against Candida Spp. Isolated from Blood Stream Infections. J Clin Diagn Res. 2016 Aug;10(8):DC09-11. doi: 10.7860/JCDR/2016/19958.8339. Epub 2016 Aug 1. PMID: 27656437; PMCID: PMC5028442.

20. Ahmad N, Alam MK, Shehbaz A, Khan A, Mannan A, Hakim SR, Bisht D, Owais M. Antimicrobial activity of clove oil and its potential in the treatment of vaginal candidiasis. J Drug Target. 2005 Dec;13(10):555-61. doi: 10.1080/10611860500422958. PMID: 16390816.

21. Aghazadeh M, Zahedi Bialvaei A, Aghazadeh M, Kabiri F, Saliani N, Yousefi M, Eslami H, Samadi Kafil H. Survey of the Antibiofilm and Antimicrobial Effects of Zingiber officinale (in Vitro Study). Jundishapur J Microbiol. 2016 Feb 7;9(2):e30167. doi: 10.5812/jjm.30167. PMID: 27127591; PMCID: PMC4842230.

22. Setty JV, Srinivasan I, Sathiesh RT, Kale M, Shetty VV, Venkatesh S. In vitro evaluation of antimicrobial effect of Myristica fragrans on common endodontic pathogens. J Indian Soc

Pedod Prev Dent. 2020 Apr-Jun;38(2):145-151. doi: 10.4103/JISPPD.JISPPD_214_20. PMID: 32611860.

23. Peedikayil FC, Sreenivasan P, Narayanan A. Effect of coconut oil in plaque related gingivitis – A preliminary report. Niger Med J. 2015 Mar-Apr;56(2):143-7. doi: 10.4103/0300-1652.153406. PMID: 25838632; PMCID: PMC4382606.

24. Ogbolu DO, Oni AA, Daini OA, Oloko AP. In vitro antimicrobial properties of coconut oil on Candida species in Ibadan, Nigeria. J Med Food. 2007 Jun;10(2):384-7. doi: 10.1089/jmf.2006.1209. PMID: 17651080.

25. Verallo-Rowell VM, Dillague KM, Syah-Tjundawan BS. Novel antibacterial and emollient effects of coconut and virgin olive oils in adult atopic dermatitis. Dermatitis. 2008 Nov-Dec;19(6):308-15. PMID: 19134433.

26. Singh VK, Jaswal BS, Sharma J, Rai PK. Analysis of stones formed in the human gall bladder and kidney using advanced spectroscopic techniques. Biophys Rev. 2020 Jun;12(3):647-668. doi: 10.1007/s12551-020-00697-2. Epub 2020 May 14. PMID: 32410185; PMCID: PMC7311631.

27. McMillin M, DeMorrow S. Effects of bile acids on neurological function and disease. FASEB J. 2016 Nov;30(11):3658-3668. doi: 10.1096/fj.201600275R. Epub 2016 Jul 28. PMID: 27468758; PMCID: PMC5067249.

28. Jarius S, Paul F, Weinshenker BG, Levy M, Kim HJ, Wildemann B. Neuromyelitis optica. Nat Rev Dis Primers. 2020 Oct 22;6(1):85. doi: 10.1038/s41572-020-0214-9. PMID: 33093467.

29. Hrubisko M, Danis R, Huorka M, Wawruch M. Histamine Intolerance-The More We Know the Less We Know. A Review. Nutrients. 2021 Jun 29;13(7):2228. doi: 10.3390/nu13072228. PMID: 34209583; PMCID: PMC8308327.

30. Sasahara I, Fujimura N, Nozawa Y, Furuhata Y, Sato H. The effect of histidine on mental fatigue and cognitive performance in subjects with high fatigue and sleep disruption scores. Physiol Behav. 2015 Aug 1;147:238-44. doi: 10.1016/j.physbeh.2015.04.042. Epub 2015 Apr 25. PMID: 25921948.

31. Hoddy KK, Kroeger CM, Trepanowski JF, Barnosky AR, Bhutani S, Varady KA. Safety of alternate day fasting and effect on disordered eating behaviors. Nutr J. 2015 May 6;14:44. doi: 10.1186/s12937-015-0029-9. PMID: 25943396; PMCID: PMC4424827.

32. Varady KA, Gabel K. Safety and efficacy of alternate day fasting. Nat Rev Endocrinol. 2019 Dec;15(12):686-687. doi: 10.1038/s41574-019-0270-y. PMID: 31558778.

33. Cui Y, Cai T, Zhou Z, Mu Y, Lu Y, Gao Z, Wu J, Zhang Y. Health Effects of Alternate-Day Fasting in Adults: A Systematic Review and Meta-Analysis. Front Nutr. 2020 Nov 24;7:586036. doi: 10.3389/fnut.2020.586036. PMID: 33330587; PMCID: PMC7732631.

34. Kumamoto CA. Inflammation and gastrointestinal Candida colonization. Curr Opin Microbiol. 2011 Aug;14(4):386-91. doi: 10.1016/j.mib.2011.07.015. Epub 2011 Jul 28. PMID: 21802979; PMCID: PMC3163673.

35. Ait Chait Y, Mottawea W, Tompkins TA, Hammami R. Unravelling the antimicrobial action of antidepressants on gut commensal microbes. Sci Rep. 2020 Oct 21;10(1):17878. doi: 10.1038/s41598-020-74934-9. PMID: 33087796; PMCID: PMC7578019.

36. https://www.accessdata.fda.gov/drugsatfda_docs/label/2019/020936s047lbl.pdf

37. Arterburn D, Sofer T, Boudreau DM, Bogart A, Westbrook EO, Theis MK, Simon G, Haneuse S. Long-Term Weight Change after Initiating Second-Generation Antidepressants. J Clin Med. 2016 Apr 13;5(4):48. doi: 10.3390/jcm5040048. PMID: 27089374; PMCID: PMC4850471.

38. Kirsch I. Antidepressants and the Placebo Effect. Z Psychol. 2014;222(3):128-134. doi: 10.1027/2151-2604/a000176. PMID: 25279271; PMCID: PMC4172306.

39. Bikle DD. Vitamin D: an ancient hormone. Exp Dermatol. 2011 Jan;20(1):7-13. doi: 10.1111/j.1600-0625.2010.01202.x. PMID: 21197695.

40. Garland CF, Kim JJ, Mohr SB, Gorham ED, Grant WB, Giovannucci EL, Baggerly L, Hofflich H, Ramsdell JW, Zeng K, Heaney RP. Meta-analysis of all-cause mortality according to serum 25-hydroxyvitamin D. Am J Public Health. 2014 Aug;104(8):e43-50. doi: 10.2105/AJPH.2014.302034. Epub 2014 Jun 12. PMID: 24922127; PMCID: PMC4103214.

41. Schöttker B, Haug U, Schomburg L, Köhrle J, Perna L, Müller H, Holleczek B, Brenner H. Strong associations of 25-hydroxyvitamin D concentrations with all-cause, cardiovascular, cancer, and respiratory disease mortality in a large cohort study. Am J Clin Nutr. 2013 Apr;97(4):782-93. doi: 10.3945/ajcn.112.047712. Epub 2013 Feb 27. PMID: 23446902.

42. Karadeniz Y, Özpamuk-Karadeniz F, Ahbab S, Ataoğlu E, Can G. Vitamin D Deficiency Is a Potential Risk for Blood Pressure Elevation and the Development of Hypertension. Medicina (Kaunas). 2021 Nov 25;57(12):1297. doi: 10.3390/medicina57121297. PMID: 34946242; PMCID: PMC8703486.

43. Xie F, Huang T, Lou D, Fu R, Ni C, Hong J, Ruan L. Effect of vitamin D supplementation on the incidence and prognosis of depression: An updated meta-analysis based on randomized controlled trials. Front Public Health. 2022 Aug 1;10:903547. doi: 10.3389/fpubh.2022.903547. PMID: 35979473; PMCID: PMC9376678.

44. Gominak SC. Vitamin D deficiency changes the intestinal microbiome reducing B vitamin production in the gut. The resulting lack of pantothenic acid adversely affects the immune system, producing a "proinflammatory" state associated with atherosclerosis and autoimmunity. Med Hypotheses. 2016 Sep;94:103-7. doi: 10.1016/j.mehy.2016.07.007. Epub 2016 Jul 14. PMID: 27515213.

45. Borsche L, Glauner B, von Mendel J. COVID-19 Mortality Risk Correlates Inversely with Vitamin D3 Status, and a Mortality Rate Close to Zero Could Theoretically Be Achieved at 50 ng/mL 25(OH)D3: Results of a Systematic Review and Meta-Analysis. Nutrients. 2021 Oct 14;13(10):3596. doi: 10.3390/nu13103596. PMID: 34684596; PMCID: PMC8541492.

46. Rinninella E, Raoul P, Cintoni M, Franceschi F, Miggiano GAD, Gasbarrini A, Mele MC. What is the Healthy Gut Microbiota Composition? A Changing Ecosystem across Age, Environment, Diet, and Diseases. Microorganisms. 2019 Jan 10;7(1):14. doi: 10.3390/microorganisms7010014. PMID: 30634578; PMCID: PMC6351938.

47. McCullough PJ, Lehrer DS, Amend J. Daily oral dosing of vitamin D3 using 5000 TO 50,000 international units a day in long-term hospitalized patients: Insights from a seven year experience. J Steroid Biochem Mol Biol. 2019 May;189:228-239. doi: 10.1016/j.jsbmb.2018.12.010. Epub 2019 Jan 4. PMID: 30611908.

48. Ellis S, Tsiopanis G, Lad T. Risks of the 'Sunshine pill' - a case of hypervitaminosis D. Clin Med (Lond). 2018 Aug;18(4):311-313. doi: 10.7861/clinmedicine.18-4-311. PMID: 30072556; PMCID: PMC6334045.

49. Jadhav N, Ajgaonkar S, Saha P, Gurav P, Pandey A, Basudkar V, Gada Y, Panda S, Jadhav S, Mehta D, Nair S. Molecular Pathways and Roles for Vitamin K2-7 as a Health-Beneficial Nutraceutical: Challenges and Opportunities. Front Pharmacol. 2022 Jun 14;13:896920. doi: 10.3389/fphar.2022.896920. PMID: 35774605; PMCID: PMC9237441.

50. Jadhav N, Ajgaonkar S, Saha P, Gurav P, Pandey A, Basudkar V, Gada Y, Panda S, Jadhav S, Mehta D, Nair S. Molecular Pathways and Roles for Vitamin K2-7 as a Health-Beneficial Nutraceutical: Challenges and Opportunities. Front Pharmacol. 2022 Jun 14;13:896920. doi: 10.3389/fphar.2022.896920. PMID: 35774605; PMCID: PMC9237441.

51. Martel JL, Kerndt CC, Doshi H, Franklin DS. Vitamin B1 (Thiamine). 2022 Aug 27. In: StatPearls [Internet]. Treasure Island (FL): StatPearls Publishing; 2022 Jan–. PMID: 29493982.

52. Suwannasom N, Kao I, Pruß A, Georgieva R, Bäumler H. Riboflavin: The Health Benefits of a Forgotten Natural Vitamin. Int J Mol Sci. 2020 Jan 31;21(3):950. doi: 10.3390/ijms21030950. PMID: 32023913; PMCID: PMC7037471.

53. Gasperi V, Sibilano M, Savini I, Catani MV. Niacin in the Central Nervous System: An Update of Biological Aspects and Clinical Applications. Int J Mol Sci. 2019 Feb 23;20(4):974. doi: 10.3390/ijms20040974. PMID: 30813414; PMCID: PMC6412771.

54. Habibe MN, Kellar JZ. Niacin Toxicity. 2022 Jul 26. In: StatPearls [Internet]. Treasure Island (FL): StatPearls Publishing; 2022 Jan–. PMID: 32644563

55. Sanvictores T, Chauhan S. Vitamin B5 (Pantothenic Acid). 2022 Oct 12. In: StatPearls [Internet]. Treasure Island (FL): StatPearls Publishing; 2022 Jan–. PMID: 33085380.

56. Stach K, Stach W, Augoff K. Vitamin B6 in Health and Disease. Nutrients. 2021 Sep 17;13(9):3229. doi: 10.3390/nu13093229. PMID: 34579110; PMCID: PMC8467949.

57. Hemminger A, Wills BK. Vitamin B6 Toxicity. 2022 Apr 14. In: StatPearls [Internet]. Treasure Island (FL): StatPearls Publishing; 2022 Jan–. PMID: 32119387.

58. Agrawal S, Agrawal A, Said HM. Biotin deficiency enhances the inflammatory response of human dendritic cells. Am J Physiol Cell Physiol. 2016 Sep 1;311(3):C386-91. doi: 10.1152/ajpcell.00141.2016. Epub 2016 Jul 13. PMID: 27413170; PMCID: PMC5129763.

59. Bistas KG, Tadi P. Biotin. [Updated 2022 Jul 4]. In: StatPearls [Internet]. Treasure Island (FL): StatPearls Publishing; 2022 Jan–. Available from: https://www.ncbi.nlm.nih.gov/books/NBK554493/

60. Zsigrai S, Kalmár A, Valcz G, Szigeti KA, Barták BK, Nagy ZB, Igaz P, Tulassay Z, Molnár B. A B9-vitamin élettani és kórélettani jelentősége. Összegzés a folsav táplálékkiegészítőként történő alkalmazásának 30. évfordulójára [Physiological and pathophysiological significance of vitamin B9. Summary on the occasion of the 30-year introduction of folic acid as a dietary supplement]. Orv Hetil. 2019 Jul;160(28):1087-1096. Hungarian. doi: 10.1556/650.2019.31441. PMID: 31280597.

61. Ankar A, Kumar A. Vitamin B12 Deficiency. [Updated 2022 Oct 22]. In: StatPearls [Internet]. Treasure Island (FL): StatPearls Publishing; 2022 Jan–. Available from: https://www.ncbi.nlm.nih.gov/books/NBK441923/

62. Allen LH. Vitamin B-12. Adv Nutr. 2012 Jan;3(1):54-5. doi: 10.3945/an.111.001370. Epub 2012 Jan 5. PMID: 22332101; PMCID: PMC3262614.

63. Institute of Medicine (US) Standing Committee on the Scientific Evaluation of Dietary Reference Intakes and its Panel on Folate, Other B Vitamins, and Choline. Dietary Reference Intakes for Thiamin, Riboflavin, Niacin, Vitamin B6, Folate, Vitamin B12, Pantothenic Acid, Biotin, and Choline. Washington (DC): National Academies Press (US); 1998. Available from: https://www.ncbi.nlm.nih.gov/books/NBK114310/ doi: 10.17226/6015

64. Eftekhari K, Vahedi Z, Kamali Aghdam M, Noemi Diaz D. A Randomized Double-Blind Placebo-Controlled Trial of Lactobacillus reuteri for Chronic Functional Abdominal Pain in Children. Iran J Pediatr. 2015 Dec;25(6):e2616. doi: 10.5812/ijp.2616. Epub 2015 Dec 23. PMID: 26635937; PMCID: PMC4662837.

65. Sun J, Qiao Y, Qi C, Jiang W, Xiao H, Shi Y, Le GW. High-fat-diet-induced obesity is associated with decreased anti-inflammatory Lactobacillus reuteri sensitive to oxidative stress in mouse Peyer's patches. Nutrition. 2016 Feb;32(2):265-72. doi: 10.1016/j.nut.2015.08.020. Epub 2015 Sep 25. PMID: 26620713.

66. Bindels LB, Neyrinck AM, Claus SP, Le Roy CI, Grangette C, Pot B, Martinez I, Walter J, Cani PD, Delzenne NM. Synbiotic approach restores intestinal homeostasis and prolongs survival in

leukaemic mice with cachexia. ISME J. 2016 Jun;10(6):1456-70. doi: 10.1038/ismej.2015.209. Epub 2015 Nov 27. PMID: 26613342; PMCID: PMC5029183.

67. Mackos AR, Galley JD, Eubank TD, Easterling RS, Parry NM, Fox JG, Lyte M, Bailey MT. Social stress-enhanced severity of Citrobacter rodentium-induced colitis is CCL2-dependent and attenuated by probiotic Lactobacillus reuteri. Mucosal Immunol. 2016 Mar;9(2):515-26. doi: 10.1038/mi.2015.81. Epub 2015 Sep 30. PMID: 26422754; PMCID: PMC4794400.

68. Tian F, Chi F, Wang G, Liu X, Zhang Q, Chen Y, Zhang H, Chen W. Lactobacillus rhamnosus CCFM1107 treatment ameliorates alcohol-induced liver injury in a mouse model of chronic alcohol feeding. J Microbiol. 2015 Dec;53(12):856-63. doi: 10.1007/s12275-015-5239-5. Epub 2015 Dec 2. PMID: 26626356.

69. Divyashri G, Krishna G, Muralidhara, Prapulla SG. Probiotic attributes, antioxidant, anti-inflammatory and neuromodulatory effects of Enterococcus faecium CFR 3003: in vitro and in vivo evidence. J Med Microbiol. 2015 Dec;64(12):1527-1540. doi: 10.1099/jmm.0.000184. Epub 2015 Oct 7. PMID: 26450608.

70. Grompone G, Martorell P, Llopis S, González N, Genovés S, Mulet AP, Fernández-Calero T, Tiscornia I, Bollati-Fogolín M, Chambaud I, Foligné B, Montserrat A, Ramón D. Anti-inflammatory Lactobacillus rhamnosus CNCM I-3690 strain protects against oxidative stress and increases lifespan in Caenorhabditis elegans. PLoS One. 2012;7(12):e52493. doi: 10.1371/journal.pone.0052493. Epub 2012 Dec 26. PMID: 23300685; PMCID: PMC3530454.

71. Affhan S, Dachang W, Xin Y, Shang D. Lactic acid bacteria protect human intestinal epithelial cells from Staphylococcus aureus and Pseudomonas aeruginosa infections. Genet Mol Res. 2015 Dec 16;14(4):17044-58. doi: 10.4238/2015.December.16.5. PMID: 26681052.

72. Deepak V, Ramachandran S, Balahmar RM, Pandian SR, Sivasubramaniam SD, Nellaiah H, Sundar K. In vitro evaluation of anticancer properties of exopolysaccharides from Lactobacillus acidophilus in colon cancer cell lines. In Vitro Cell Dev Biol Anim. 2016 Feb;52(2):163-73. doi: 10.1007/s11626-015-9970-3. Epub 2015 Dec 10. PMID: 26659393.

73. Sahay B, Ge Y, Colliou N, Zadeh M, Weiner C, Mila A, Owen JL, Mohamadzadeh M. Advancing the use of Lactobacillus acidophilus surface layer protein A for the treatment of intestinal disorders in humans. Gut Microbes. 2015;6(6):392-7. doi: 10.1080/19490976.2015.1107697. Erratum in: Addendum to: Lightfoot YL, Selle K, Yang T, Goh YJ, Sahay B, Zadeh M, Owen JL, Colliou N, Li E, Johannssen T, Lepenies B, Klaenhammer TR, Mohamadzadeh M. SIGNR3-dependent immune regulation by Lactobacillus acidophilus-Surface layer protein A in Colitis. EMBO Journal 2015 Apr 1;34(7):881-95; PMID: 2566591; PMCID: PMC4388597. PMID: 26647142; PMCID: PMC4826124.

74. Xie J, Yu Q, Nie S, Fan S, Xiong T, Xie M. Effects of Lactobacillus plantarum NCU116 on Intestine Mucosal Immunity in Immunosuppressed Mice. J Agric Food Chem. 2015 Dec 30;63(51):10914-20. doi: 10.1021/acs.jafc.5b04757. Epub 2015 Dec 18. PMID: 26651209.

75. Liu YW, Liu WH, Wu CC, Juan YC, Wu YC, Tsai HP, Wang S, Tsai YC. Psychotropic effects of Lactobacillus plantarum PS128 in early life-stressed and naïve adult mice. Brain Res. 2016 Jan 15;1631:1-12. doi: 10.1016/j.brainres.2015.11.018. Epub 2015 Nov 24. PMID: 26620542.

76. Dyer KD, Drummond RA, Rice TA, Percopo CM, Brenner TA, Barisas DA, Karpe KA, Moore ML, Rosenberg HF. Priming of the Respiratory Tract with Immunobiotic Lactobacillus plantarum Limits Infection of Alveolar Macrophages with Recombinant Pneumonia Virus of Mice (rK2-PVM). J Virol. 2015 Nov 4;90(2):979-91. doi: 10.1128/JVI.02279-15. PMID: 26537680; PMCID: PMC4702661.

77. Yunes RA, Klimina KM, Emelyanov KV, Zakharevich NV, Poluektova EU, Danilenko VN. Draft Genome Sequences of Lactobacillus plantarum Strain 90sk and Lactobacillus brevis Strain 15f: Focusing on Neurotransmitter Genes. Genome Announc. 2015 Apr 16;3(2):e00261-15. doi: 10.1128/genomeA.00261-15. PMID: 25883284; PMCID: PMC4400427.

78. GABA: https://examine.com/supplements/GABA/

79. Yakovlieva M, Tacheva T, Mihaylova S, Tropcheva R, Trifonova K, Toleкova A, Danova S, Vlaykova T. Influence of Lactobacillus brevis 15 and Lactobacillus plantarum 13 on blood glucose and body weight in rats after high-fructose diet. Benef Microbes. 2015;6(4):505-12. doi: 10.3920/BM2014.0012. Epub 2015 Apr 22. PMID: 25691100.

80. Tanaka Y, Takami K, Nishijima T, Aoki R, Mawatari T, Ikeda T. Short- and long-term dynamics in the intestinal microbiota following ingestion of Bifidobacterium animalis subsp. lactis GCL2505. Biosci Microbiota Food Health. 2015;34(4):77-85. doi: 10.12938/bmfh.2015-001. Epub 2015 Jul 31. PMID: 26594607; PMCID: PMC4639512.

81. Eskesen D, Jespersen L, Michelsen B, Whorwell PJ, Müller-Lissner S, Morberg CM. Effect of the probiotic strain Bifidobacterium animalis subsp. lactis, BB-12®, on defecation frequency in healthy subjects with low defecation frequency and abdominal discomfort: a randomised, double-blind, placebo-controlled, parallel-group trial. Br J Nutr. 2015 Nov 28;114(10):1638-46. doi: 10.1017/S0007114515003347. Epub 2015 Sep 18. PMID: 26382580; PMCID: PMC4657032.

82. Steenbergen L, Sellaro R, van Hemert S, Bosch JA, Colzato LS. A randomized controlled trial to test the effect of multispecies probiotics on cognitive reactivity to sad mood. Brain Behav Immun. 2015 Aug;48:258-64. doi: 10.1016/j.bbi.2015.04.003. Epub 2015 Apr 7. PMID: 25862297.

83. Katz MJ, Derby CA, Wang C, Sliwinski MJ, Ezzati A, Zimmerman ME, Zwerling JL, Lipton RB. Influence of Perceived Stress on Incident Amnestic Mild Cognitive Impairment: Results From the Einstein Aging Study. Alzheimer Dis Assoc Disord. 2016 Apr-Jun;30(2):93-8. doi: 10.1097/WAD.0000000000000125. PMID: 26655068; PMCID: PMC4877262.

84. Sugahara H, Odamaki T, Fukuda S, Kato T, Xiao JZ, Abe F, Kikuchi J, Ohno H. Probiotic Bifidobacterium longum alters gut luminal metabolism through modification of the gut microbial community. Sci Rep. 2015 Aug 28;5:13548. doi: 10.1038/srep13548. PMID: 26315217; PMCID: PMC4552000.

85. Parvaneh K, Ebrahimi M, Sabran MR, Karimi G, Hwei AN, Abdul-Majeed S, Ahmad Z, Ibrahim Z, Jamaluddin R. Probiotics (Bifidobacterium longum) Increase Bone Mass Density and Upregulate Sparc and Bmp-2 Genes in Rats with Bone Loss Resulting from Ovariectomy. Biomed Res Int. 2015;2015:897639. doi: 10.1155/2015/897639. Epub 2015 Aug 20. PMID: 26366421; PMCID: PMC4558422.

86. Leclercq S, Matamoros S, Cani PD, Neyrinck AM, Jamar F, Stärkel P, Windey K, Tremaroli V, Bäckhed F, Verbeke K, de Timary P, Delzenne NM. Intestinal permeability, gut-bacterial dysbiosis, and behavioral markers of alcohol-dependence severity. Proc Natl Acad Sci U S A. 2014 Oct 21;111(42):E4485-93. doi: 10.1073/pnas.1415174111. Epub 2014 Oct 6. PMID: 25288760; PMCID: PMC4210345.

87. Spreadbury I. Comparison with ancestral diets suggests dense acellular carbohydrates promote an inflammatory microbiota, and may be the primary dietary cause of leptin resistance and obesity. Diabetes Metab Syndr Obes. 2012;5:175-89. doi: 10.2147/DMSO.S33473. Epub 2012 Jul 6. PMID: 22826636; PMCID: PMC3402009.

88. Novak EA, Mollen KP. Mitochondrial dysfunction in inflammatory bowel disease. Front Cell Dev Biol. 2015 Oct 1;3:62. doi: 10.3389/fcell.2015.00062. PMID: 26484345; PMCID: PMC4589667.

89. Devkota S, Wang Y, Musch MW, Leone V, Fehlner-Peach H, Nadimpalli A, Antonopoulos DA, Jabri B, Chang EB. Dietary-fat-induced taurocholic acid promotes pathobiont expansion and Colitis in Il10-/- mice. Nature. 2012 Jul 5;487(7405):104-8. doi: 10.1038/nature11225. PMID: 22722865; PMCID: PMC3393783.

90. von Woedtke T, Schlüter B, Pflegel P, Lindequist U, Jülich WD. Aspects of the antimicrobial efficacy of grapefruit seed extract and its relation to preservative substances contained. Pharmazie. 1999 Jun;54(6):452-6. PMID: 10399191.

91. Ranabir S, Reetu K. Stress and hormones. Indian J Endocrinol Metab. 2011 Jan;15(1):18-22. doi: 10.4103/2230-8210.77573. PMID: 21584161; PMCID: PMC3079864.

92. Lovallo WR, Whitsett TL, al'Absi M, Sung BH, Vincent AS, Wilson MF. Caffeine stimulation of cortisol secretion across the waking hours in relation to caffeine intake levels. Psychosom Med. 2005 Sep-Oct;67(5):734-9. doi: 10.1097/01.psy.0000181270.20036.06. PMID: 16204431; PMCID: PMC2257922.

93. Blumstein GW, Parsa A, Park AK, McDowell BL, Arroyo-Mendoza M, Girguis M, Adler-Moore JP, Olson J, Buckley NE. Effect of Delta-9-tetrahydrocannabinol on mouse resistance to systemic Candida albicans infection. PLoS One. 2014 Jul 24;9(7):e103288. doi: 10.1371/journal.pone.0103288. PMID: 25057822; PMCID: PMC4110019.

94. Reiss CS. Cannabinoids and Viral Infections. Pharmaceuticals (Basel). 2010 Jun 1;3(6):1873-1886. doi: 10.3390/ph3061873. PMID: 20634917; PMCID: PMC2903762.

95. Kozela E, Lev N, Kaushansky N, Eilam R, Rimmerman N, Levy R, Ben-Nun A, Juknat A, Vogel Z. Cannabidiol inhibits pathogenic T cells, decreases spinal microglial activation and

ameliorates multiple sclerosis-like disease in C57BL/6 mice. Br J Pharmacol. 2011 Aug;163(7):1507-19. doi: 10.1111/j.1476-5381.2011.01379.x. PMID: 21449980; PMCID: PMC3165959.

96. De Filippis D, Esposito G, Cirillo C, Cipriano M, De Winter BY, Scuderi C, Sarnelli G, Cuomo R, Steardo L, De Man JG, Iuvone T. Cannabidiol reduces intestinal inflammation through the control of neuroimmune axis. PLoS One. 2011;6(12):e28159. doi: 10.1371/journal.pone.0028159. Epub 2011 Dec 6. PMID: 22163000; PMCID: PMC3232190.

97. Javadov S, Kozlov AV, Camara AKS. Mitochondria in Health and Diseases. Cells. 2020 May 9;9(5):1177. doi: 10.3390/cells9051177. PMID: 32397376; PMCID: PMC7290976.

98. Jonscher KR, Chowanadisai W, Rucker RB. Pyrroloquinoline-Quinone Is More Than an Antioxidant: A Vitamin-like Accessory Factor Important in Health and Disease Prevention. Biomolecules. 2021 Sep 30;11(10):1441. doi: 10.3390/biom11101441. PMID: 34680074; PMCID: PMC8533503.

99. Chen CT, Kitson AP, Hopperton KE, Domenichiello AF, Trépanier MO, Lin LE, Ermini L, Post M, Thies F, Bazinet RP. Plasma non-esterified docosahexaenoic acid is the major pool supplying the brain. Sci Rep. 2015 Oct 29;5:15791. doi: 10.1038/srep15791. PMID: 26511533; PMCID: PMC4625162.

100. Siegert E, Paul F, Rothe M, Weylandt KH. The effect of omega-3 fatty acids on central nervous system remyelination in fat-1 mice. BMC Neurosci. 2017 Jan 24;18(1):19. doi: 10.1186/s12868-016-0312-5. PMID: 28114887; PMCID: PMC5259863.

101. Jenkins TA, Nguyen JC, Polglaze KE, Bertrand PP. Influence of Tryptophan and Serotonin on Mood and Cognition with a Possible Role of the Gut-Brain Axis. Nutrients. 2016 Jan 20;8(1):56. doi: 10.3390/nu8010056. PMID: 26805875; PMCID: PMC4728667.

102. Yusufu I, Ding K, Smith K, Wankhade UD, Sahay B, Patterson GT, Pacholczyk R, Adusumilli S, Hamrick MW, Hill WD, Isales CM, Fulzele S. A Tryptophan-Deficient Diet Induces Gut Microbiota Dysbiosis and Increases Systemic Inflammation in Aged Mice. Int J Mol Sci. 2021 May 8;22(9):5005. doi: 10.3390/ijms22095005. PMID: 34066870; PMCID: PMC8125914.

103. DiNicolantonio JJ, O'Keefe JH, Wilson W. Subclinical magnesium deficiency: a principal driver of cardiovascular disease and a public health crisis. Open Heart. 2018 Jan 13;5(1):e000668. doi: 10.1136/openhrt-2017-000668. Erratum in: Open Heart. 2018 Apr 5;5(1):e000668corr1. PMID: 29387426; PMCID: PMC5786912.

104. Allerton TD, Proctor DN, Stephens JM, Dugas TR, Spielmann G, Irving BA. l-Citrulline Supplementation: Impact on Cardiometabolic Health. Nutrients. 2018 Jul 19;10(7):921. doi: 10.3390/nu10070921. PMID: 30029482; PMCID: PMC6073798.

105. Kim VY, Batty A, Li J, Kirk SG, Crowell SA, Jin Y, Tang J, Zhang J, Rogers LK, Deng HX, Nelin LD, Liu Y. Glutathione Reductase Promotes Fungal Clearance and Suppresses Inflammation during Systemic Candida albicans Infection in Mice. J Immunol. 2019 Oct 15;203(8):2239-2251. doi: 10.4049/jimmunol.1701686. Epub 2019 Sep 9. PMID: 31501257; PMCID: PMC6783371.

106. Cleveland WL, DeLaPaz RL, Fawwaz RA, Challop RS. High-dose glycine treatment of refractory obsessive-compulsive disorder and body dysmorphic disorder in a 5-year period. Neural Plast. 2009;2009:768398. doi: 10.1155/2009/768398. Epub 2010 Feb 18. PMID: 20182547; PMCID: PMC2825652.

107. Holeček M. Side effects of amino acid supplements. Physiol Res. 2022 Mar 25;71(1):29-45. doi: 10.33549/physiolres.934790. Epub 2022 Jan 19. PMID: 35043647; PMCID: PMC8997670.

108. Gut P, Lizzo G, Migliavacca E, Karagounis L, Heise T, Eynatten M. Effects of glycine and n-acetylcysteine on glutathione levels and mitochondrial energy metabolism in healthy aging. Innov Aging. 2021 Dec 17;5(Suppl 1):685. doi: 10.1093/geroni/igab046.2574. PMCID: PMC8968300.

109. Meléndez-Hevia E, De Paz-Lugo P, Cornish-Bowden A, Cárdenas ML. A weak link in metabolism: the metabolic capacity for glycine biosynthesis does not satisfy the need for collagen synthesis. J Biosci. 2009 Dec;34(6):853-72. doi: 10.1007/s12038-009-0100-9. PMID: 20093739.

110. Lan Y, Zhu W, Duan X, Deng T, Li S, Liu Y, Yang Z, Wen Y, Luo L, Zhao S, Wang J, Zhao Z, Wu W, Zeng G. Glycine suppresses kidney calcium oxalate crystal depositions via regulating urinary excretions of oxalate and citrate. J Cell Physiol. 2021 Oct;236(10):6824-6835. doi: 10.1002/jcp.30370. Epub 2021 Mar 27. PMID: 33772775.

111. Alves A, Bassot A, Bulteau AL, Pirola L, Morio B. Glycine Metabolism and Its Alterations in Obesity and Metabolic Diseases. Nutrients. 2019 Jun 16;11(6):1356. doi: 10.3390/nu11061356. PMID: 31208147; PMCID: PMC6627940.

112. Díaz-Flores M, Cruz M, Duran-Reyes G, Munguia-Miranda C, Loza-Rodríguez H, Pulido-Casas E, Torres-Ramírez N, Gaja-Rodriguez O, Kumate J, Baiza-Gutman LA, Hernández-Saavedra D. Oral supplementation with glycine reduces oxidative stress in patients with metabolic syndrome, improving their systolic blood pressure. Can J Physiol Pharmacol. 2013 Oct;91(10):855-60. doi: 10.1139/cjpp-2012-0341. Epub 2013 Jun 17. PMID: 24144057.

113. de Paz-Lugo P, Lupiáñez JA, Meléndez-Hevia E. High glycine concentration increases collagen synthesis by articular chondrocytes in vitro: acute glycine deficiency could be an important cause of osteoarthritis. Amino Acids. 2018 Oct;50(10):1357-1365. doi: 10.1007/s00726-018-2611-x. Epub 2018 Jul 13. PMID: 30006659; PMCID: PMC6153947.

114. Johnson AA, Cuellar TL. Glycine and aging: Evidence and mechanisms. Ageing Res Rev. 2023 Jun;87:101922. doi: 10.1016/j.arr.2023.101922. Epub 2023 Mar 31. PMID: 37004845.

115. Díaz-Flores M, Cruz M, Duran-Reyes G, Munguia-Miranda C, Loza-Rodríguez H, Pulido-Casas E, Torres-Ramírez N, Gaja-Rodriguez O, Kumate J, Baiza-Gutman LA, Hernández-Saavedra D. Oral supplementation with glycine reduces oxidative stress in patients with metabolic syndrome, improving their systolic blood pressure. Can J Physiol Pharmacol. 2013 Oct;91(10):855-60. doi: 10.1139/cjpp-2012-0341. Epub 2013 Jun 17. PMID: 24144057.

116. Howard A, Tahir I, Javed S, Waring SM, Ford D, Hirst BH. Glycine transporter GLYT1 is essential for glycine-mediated protection of human intestinal epithelial cells against oxidative damage. J Physiol. 2010 Mar 15;588(Pt 6):995-1009. doi: 10.1113/jphysiol.2009.186262. Epub 2010 Feb 1. PMID: 20123783; PMCID: PMC2849964.

117. Alves A, Bassot A, Bulteau AL, Pirola L, Morio B. Glycine Metabolism and Its Alterations in Obesity and Metabolic Diseases. Nutrients. 2019 Jun 16;11(6):1356. doi: 10.3390/nu11061356. PMID: 31208147; PMCID: PMC6627940.

118. Cai CC, Zhu JH, Ye LX, Dai YY, Fang MC, Hu YY, Pan SL, Chen S, Li PJ, Fu XQ, Lin ZL. Glycine Protects against Hypoxic-Ischemic Brain Injury by Regulating Mitochondria-Mediated Autophagy via the AMPK Pathway. Oxid Med Cell Longev. 2019 Feb 6;2019:4248529. doi: 10.1155/2019/4248529. PMID: 30881590; PMCID: PMC6381570.

119. Yusufu I, Ding K, Smith K, Wankhade UD, Sahay B, Patterson GT, Pacholczyk R, Adusumilli S, Hamrick MW, Hill WD, Isales CM, Fulzele S. A Tryptophan-Deficient Diet Induces Gut Microbiota Dysbiosis and Increases Systemic Inflammation in Aged Mice. Int J Mol Sci. 2021 May 8;22(9):5005. doi: 10.3390/ijms22095005. PMID: 34066870; PMCID: PMC8125914.

120. Richard DM, Dawes MA, Mathias CW, Acheson A, Hill-Kapturczak N, Dougherty DM. L-Tryptophan: Basic Metabolic Functions, Behavioral Research and Therapeutic Indications. Int J Tryptophan Res. 2009 Mar 23;2:45-60. doi: 10.4137/ijtr.s2129. PMID: 20651948; PMCID: PMC2908021.

121. Richard DM, Dawes MA, Mathias CW, Acheson A, Hill-Kapturczak N, Dougherty DM. L-Tryptophan: Basic Metabolic Functions, Behavioral Research and Therapeutic Indications. Int J Tryptophan Res. 2009 Mar 23;2:45-60. doi: 10.4137/ijtr.s2129. PMID: 20651948; PMCID: PMC2908021.

122. An D, Zeng Q, Zhang P, Ma Z, Zhang H, Liu Z, Li J, Ren H, Xu D. Alpha-ketoglutarate ameliorates pressure overload-induced chronic cardiac dysfunction in mice. Redox Biol. 2021 Oct;46:102088. doi: 10.1016/j.redox.2021.102088. Epub 2021 Jul 30. PMID: 34364218; PMCID: PMC8353361.

123. Matias MI, Yong CS, Foroushani A, Goldsmith C, Mongellaz C, Sezgin E, Levental KR, Talebi A, Perrault J, Rivière A, Dehairs J, Delos O, Bertand-Michel J, Portais JC, Wong M, Marie JC, Kelekar A, Kinet S, Zimmermann VS, Levental I, Yvan-Charvet L, Swinnen JV, Muljo SA, Hernandez-Vargas H, Tardito S, Taylor N, Dardalhon V. Regulatory T cell differentiation is controlled by αKG-induced alterations in mitochondrial metabolism and lipid homeostasis. Cell Rep. 2021 Nov 2;37(5):109911. doi: 10.1016/j.celrep.2021.109911. PMID: 34731632.

124. Shade C. The Science Behind NMN-A Stable, Reliable NAD+Activator and Anti-Aging Molecule. Integr Med (Encinitas). 2020 Feb;19(1):12-14. PMID: 32549859; PMCID: PMC7238909.

125. Nguyen H, Gupta V. Alpha-Lipoic Acid. [Updated 2022 Sep 26]. In: StatPearls [Internet]. Treasure Island (FL): StatPearls Publishing; 2023 Jan-. Available from: https://www.ncbi.nlm.nih.gov/books/NBK564301/.

126. Virmani MA, Cirulli M. The Role of l-Carnitine in Mitochondria, Prevention of Metabolic Inflexibility and Disease Initiation. Int J Mol Sci. 2022 Feb 28;23(5):2717. doi: 10.3390/ijms23052717. PMID: 35269860; PMCID: PMC8910660.

127. Hou Y, Wu G. Nutritionally Essential Amino Acids. Adv Nutr. 2018 Nov 1;9(6):849-851. doi: 10.1093/advances/nmy054. PMID: 30239556; PMCID: PMC6247364.

128. Allerton TD, Proctor DN, Stephens JM, Dugas TR, Spielmann G, Irving BA. l-Citrulline Supplementation: Impact on Cardiometabolic Health. Nutrients. 2018 Jul 19;10(7):921. doi: 10.3390/nu10070921. PMID: 30029482; PMCID: PMC6073798.

129. Liu D, Wang X, Kong L, Chen Z. Nicotinic acid regulates glucose and lipid metabolism through lipid independent pathways. Curr Pharm Biotechnol. 2015;16(1):3-10. doi: 10.2174/1389201015666141126123401. PMID: 25429652.

130. Lopez MJ, Mohiuddin SS. Biochemistry, Essential Amino Acids. [Updated 2023 Mar 13]. In: StatPearls [Internet]. Treasure Island (FL): StatPearls Publishing; 2023 Jan-. Available from: https://www.ncbi.nlm.nih.gov/books/NBK557845.

131. Yang D, Gouaux E. Illumination of serotonin transporter mechanism and role of the allosteric site. Sci Adv. 2021 Dec 3;7(49):eabl3857. doi: 10.1126/sciadv.abl3857. Epub 2021 Dec 1. PMID: 34851672; PMCID: PMC8635421.

132. Li Y, Yang G, Yang X, He Y, Wang W, Zhang J, Li T, Zhang W, Lin R. Nicotinic acid inhibits vascular inflammation via the SIRT1-dependent signaling pathway. J Nutr Biochem. 2015 Nov;26(11):1338-47. doi: 10.1016/j.jnutbio.2015.07.006. Epub 2015 Jul 26. PMID: 26300330.

133. Chini CCS, Peclat TR, Warner GM, Kashyap S, Espindola-Netto JM, de Oliveira GC, Gomez LS, Hogan KA, Tarragó MG, Puranik AS, Agorrody G, Thompson KL, Dang K, Clarke S, Childs BG, Kanamori KS, Witte MA, Vidal P, Kirkland AL, De Cecco M, Chellappa K, McReynolds MR, Jankowski C, Tchkonia T, Kirkland JL, Sedivy JM, van Deursen JM, Baker DJ, van Schooten W, Rabinowitz JD, Baur JA, Chini EN. CD38 ecto-enzyme in immune cells is induced during aging and regulates NAD+ and NMN levels. Nat Metab. 2020 Nov;2(11):1284-1304. doi: 10.1038/s42255-020-00298-z. Epub 2020 Nov 16. PMID: 33199925; PMCID: PMC8752031.

134. Quinzii CM, Hirano M. Coenzyme Q and mitochondrial disease. Dev Disabil Res Rev. 2010;16(2):183-8. doi: 10.1002/ddrr.108. PMID: 20818733; PMCID: PMC3097389.

135. Marshall RP, Droste JN, Giessing J, Kreider RB. Role of Creatine Supplementation in Conditions Involving Mitochondrial Dysfunction: A Narrative Review. Nutrients. 2022 Jan 26;14(3):529. doi: 10.3390/nu14030529. PMID: 35276888; PMCID: PMC8838971.

136. Eckert GP, Lipka U, Muller WE. Omega-3 fatty acids in neurodegenerative diseases: focus on mitochondria. Prostaglandins Leukot Essent Fatty Acids. 2013 Jan;88(1):105-14. doi: 10.1016/j.plefa.2012.05.006. Epub 2012 Jun 22. PMID: 22727983.

137. Depeint F, Bruce WR, Shangari N, Mehta R, O'Brien PJ. Mitochondrial function and toxicity: role of the B vitamin family on mitochondrial energy metabolism. Chem Biol Interact. 2006 Oct 27;163(1-2):94-112. doi: 10.1016/j.cbi.2006.04.014. Epub 2006 May 1. PMID: 16765926.

138. Salles J, Chanet A, Guillet C, Vaes AM, Brouwer-Brolsma EM, Rocher C, Giraudet C, Patrac V, Meugnier E, Montaurier C, Denis P, Le Bacquer O, Blot A, Jourdan M, Luiking Y, Furber M, Van Dijk M, Tardif N, Yves Boirie Y, Walrand S. Vitamin D status modulates mitochondrial oxidative capacities in skeletal muscle: role in sarcopenia. Commun Biol. 2022 Nov 24;5(1):1288. doi: 10.1038/s42003-022-04246-3. PMID: 36434267; PMCID: PMC9700804.

139. Pirinen E, Auranen M, Khan NA, Brilhante V, Urho N, Pessia A, Hakkarainen A, Kuula J, Heinonen U, Schmidt MS, Haimilahti K, Piirilä P, Lundbom N, Taskinen MR, Brenner C, Velagapudi V, Pietiläinen KH, Suomalainen A. Niacin Cures Systemic NAD+ Deficiency and Improves Muscle Performance in Adult-Onset Mitochondrial Myopathy. Cell Metab. 2020 Jun 2;31(6):1078-1090.e5. doi: 10.1016/j.cmet.2020.04.008. Epub 2020 May 7. Erratum in: Cell Metab. 2020 Jul 7;32(1):144. PMID: 32386566.

140. Killilea DW, Killilea AN. Mineral requirements for mitochondrial function: A connection to redox balance and cellular differentiation. Free Radic Biol Med. 2022 Mar;182:182-191. doi: 10.1016/j.freeradbiomed.2022.02.022. Epub 2022 Feb 24. PMID: 35218912.

141. KC S, Cárcamo JM, Golde DW. Vitamin C enters mitochondria via facilitative glucose transporter 1 (Glut1) and confers mitochondrial protection against oxidative injury. FASEB J. 2005 Oct;19(12):1657-67. doi: 10.1096/fj.05-4107com. PMID: 16195374.

142. Manzardo AM, Pendleton T, Poje A, Penick EC, Butler MG. Change in psychiatric symptomatology after benfotiamine treatment in males is related to lifetime alcoholism severity. Drug Alcohol Depend. 2015 Jul 1;152:257-63. doi: 10.1016/j.drugalcdep.2015.03.032. Epub 2015 Apr 8. PMID: 25908323; PMCID: PMC4550087.

143. Mochochoko BM, Pohl CH, O'Neill HG. Candida albicans-enteric viral interactions-The prostaglandin E2 connection and host immune responses. iScience. 2022 Dec 24;26(1):105870. doi: 10.1016/j.isci.2022.105870. PMID: 36647379; PMCID: PMC9839968.

144. Xing X, Liao Z, Tan F, Zhu Z, Jiang Y, Cao Y. Effect of Nicotinamide Against Candida albicans. Front Microbiol. 2019 Mar 26;10:595. doi: 10.3389/fmicb.2019.00595. PMID: 30972047; PMCID: PMC6443637.

145. Daniels TE, Olsen EM, Tyrka AR. Stress and Psychiatric Disorders: The Role of Mitochondria. Annu Rev Clin Psychol. 2020 May 7;16:165-186. doi: 10.1146/annurev-clinpsy-082719-104030. Epub 2020 Feb 24. PMID: 32092280; PMCID: PMC8007172.

146. Ascione C, Sala A, Mazaheri-Tehrani E, Paulone S, Palmieri B, Blasi E, Cermelli C. Herpes simplex virus-1 entrapped in Candida albicans biofilm displays decreased sensitivity to antivirals and UVA1 laser treatment. Ann Clin Microbiol Antimicrob. 2017 Nov 14;16(1):72. doi: 10.1186/s12941-017-0246-5. PMID: 29137671; PMCID: PMC5686830.

147. Muhamad R, Akrivaki A, Papagiannopoulou G, Zavridis P, Zis P. The Role of Vitamin B6 in Peripheral Neuropathy: A Systematic Review. Nutrients. 2023 Jun 21;15(13):2823. doi: 10.3390/nu15132823. PMID: 37447150; PMCID: PMC10343656.

148. Fiorindi C, Russo E, Balocchini L, Amedei A, Giudici F. Inflammatory Bowel Disease and Customized Nutritional Intervention Focusing on Gut Microbiome Balance. Nutrients. 2022 Oct 3;14(19):4117. doi: 10.3390/nu14194117. PMID: 36235770; PMCID: PMC9572914.

149. Tasnim S, Tang C, Musini VM, Wright JM. Effect of alcohol on blood pressure. Cochrane Database Syst Rev. 2020 Jul 1;7(7):CD012787. doi: 10.1002/14651858.CD012787.pub2. PMID: 32609894; PMCID: PMC8130994.

150. Manzo-Avalos S, Saavedra-Molina A. Cellular and mitochondrial effects of alcohol consumption. Int J Environ Res Public Health. 2010 Dec;7(12):4281-304. doi: 10.3390/ijerph7124281. Epub 2010 Dec 21. PMID: 21318009; PMCID: PMC3037055.

151. Hou K, Wu ZX, Chen XY, Wang JQ, Zhang D, Xiao C, Zhu D, Koya JB, Wei L, Li J, Chen ZS. Microbiota in health and diseases. Signal Transduct Target Ther. 2022 Apr 23;7(1):135. doi: 10.1038/s41392-022-00974-4. PMID: 35461318; PMCID: PMC9034083.

152. Cassidy LD, Narita M. Autophagy at the intersection of aging, senescence, and cancer. Mol Oncol. 2022 Sep;16(18):3259-3275. doi: 10.1002/1878-0261.13269. Epub 2022 Jul 9. PMID: 35689420; PMCID: PMC9490138.

153. Elmore S. Apoptosis: a review of programmed cell death. Toxicol Pathol. 2007 Jun;35(4):495-516. doi: 10.1080/01926230701320337. PMID: 17562483; PMCID: PMC2117903.

154. Fan YJ, Zong WX. The cellular decision between apoptosis and autophagy. Chin J Cancer. 2013 Mar;32(3):121-9. doi: 10.5732/cjc.012.10106. Epub 2012 Oct 10. PMID: 23114086; PMCID: PMC3845594.

155. Azizi NF, Kumar MR, Yeap SK, Abdullah JO, Khalid M, Omar AR, Osman MA, Mortadza SAS, Alitheen NB. Kefir and Its Biological Activities. Foods. 2021 May 27;10(6):1210. doi: 10.3390/foods10061210. PMID: 34071977; PMCID: PMC8226494.

156. Coelho MC, Malcata FX, Silva CCG. Lactic Acid Bacteria in Raw-Milk Cheeses: From Starter Cultures to Probiotic Functions. Foods. 2022 Jul 29;11(15):2276. doi: 10.3390/foods11152276. PMID: 35954043; PMCID: PMC9368153.

157. Mubarak Z, Humaira A, Gani BA, Muchlisin ZA. Preliminary study on the inhibitory effect of seaweed Gracilaria verrucosa extract on biofilm formation of Candida albicans cultured from the saliva of a smoker. F1000Res. 2018 May 31;7:684. doi: 10.12688/f1000research.14879.3. PMID: 30210788; PMCID: PMC6107980.

158. Singh A, D'Amico D, Andreux PA, Dunngalvin G, Kern T, Blanco-Bose W, Auwerx J, Aebischer P, Rinsch C. Direct supplementation with Urolithin A overcomes limitations of dietary exposure and gut microbiome variability in healthy adults to achieve consistent levels across the population. Eur J Clin Nutr. 2022 Feb;76(2):297-308. doi: 10.1038/s41430-021-00950-1. Epub 2021 Jun 11. PMID: 34117375; PMCID: PMC8821002.

159. Faitg J, D'Amico D, Rinsch C, Singh A. Mitophagy Activation by Urolithin A to Target Muscle Aging. Calcif Tissue Int. 2024 Jan;114(1):53-59. doi: 10.1007/s00223-023-01145-5. Epub 2023 Nov 5. PMID: 37925671; PMCID: PMC10791945.

160. Castellaro AM, Tonda A, Cejas HH, Ferreyra H, Caputto BL, Pucci OA, Gil GA. Oxalate induces breast cancer. BMC Cancer. 2015 Oct 22;15:761. doi: 10.1186/s12885-015-1747-2. PMID: 26493452; PMCID: PMC4618885.

161. Petrova P, Ivanov I, Tsigoriyna L, Valcheva N, Vasileva E, Parvanova-Mancheva T, Arsov A, Petrov K. Traditional Bulgarian Dairy Products: Ethnic Foods with Health Benefits. Microorganisms. 2021 Feb 25;9(3):480. doi: 10.3390/microorganisms9030480. PMID: 33668910; PMCID: PMC7996614.

BURRIS GUT HEALTH CHECKLIST

Name_____Date of Birth_____Age____Sex_____Today's Date_____

NOT AT ALL	SOMEWHAT		MODERATELY	A LOT
1		5		10

Please write a score of 1-10 after each question

GALLSTONES AND LIVER STONES SYMPTOM CHECKLIST	
1) Do you have pain in the upper right abdomen?	
2) Do you have pain in the mid-right side of the back?	
3) Do you feel ill after eating fatty foods?	
4) Are you frequently nauseous?	
5) Have you lost your appetite?	
6) Are your stools light in color?	
7) Is there a yellowish color to your skin or eyes?	
Total	

PARASITE SYMPTOM CHECKLIST	
1) Are you chronically tired even after several good nights' sleep?	
2) Have you had loose stools or diarrhea for more than two weeks?	
3) Do you grind your teeth or wake up frequently at night?	
4) Do you have mucus or blood in your stools?	
5) Is there undigested food in your stool?	
6) Do you experience frequent muscle and joint pain?	
7) Do you gravitate more and more toward high-sugar-content foods and	
Total	

SIBO CANDIDA IBS/GUT DYSBIOSIS SYMPTOM CHECKLIST	
1) Do you experience frequent heart palpitations?	
2) Do you struggle to concentrate or experience frequent brain fog?	
3) Do you experience frequent abdominal pain, bloating, gas, diarrhea, or constipation?	
4) Do you have frequent prostatitis (men) or yeast infections (women)?	
5) Do you have psoriasis, eczema, dermatitis, or athlete's foot?	
6) Have you become sensitive to certain foods?	
7) Do you have dizzy spells, or has your eyesight deteriorated?	
8) Do you experience involuntary muscle twitching or facial tics?	
Total	

BURRIS GUT HEALTH CHECKLIST

Name_____Date of Birth_____Age____Sex_____Today's Date_____

NOT AT ALL	SOMEWHAT	MODERATELY	A LOT
1	—————— 5	——————	10

Please write a score of 1-10 after each question

GALLSTONES AND LIVER STONES SYMPTOM CHECKLIST

1) Do you have pain in the upper right abdomen?	
2) Do you have pain in the mid-right side of the back?	
3) Do you feel ill after eating fatty foods?	
4) Are you frequently nauseous?	
5) Have you lost your appetite?	
6) Are your stools light in color?	
7) Is there a yellowish color to your skin or eyes?	
Total	

PARASITE SYMPTOM CHECKLIST

1) Are you chronically tired even after several good nights' sleep?	
2) Have you had loose stools or diarrhea for more than two weeks?	
3) Do you grind your teeth or wake up frequently at night?	
4) Do you have mucus or blood in your stools?	
5) Is there undigested food in your stool?	
6) Do you experience frequent muscle and joint pain?	
7) Do you gravitate more and more toward high-sugar-content foods and	
Total	

SIBO CANDIDA IBS/GUT DYSBIOSIS SYMPTOM CHECKLIST

1) Do you experience frequent heart palpitations?	
2) Do you struggle to concentrate or experience frequent brain fog?	
3) Do you experience frequent abdominal pain, bloating, gas, diarrhea, or constipation?	
4) Do you have frequent prostatitis (men) or yeast infections (women)?	
5) Do you have psoriasis, eczema, dermatitis, or athlete's foot?	
6) Have you become sensitive to certain foods?	
7) Do you have dizzy spells, or has your eyesight deteriorated?	
8) Do you experience involuntary muscle twitching or facial tics?	
Total	

BURRIS GUT HEALTH CHECKLIST

Name_____Date of Birth_____Age____Sex_____Today's Date_____

NOT AT ALL	SOMEWHAT		MODERATELY	A LOT
1	————————————	5	————————————	10

Please write a score of 1-10 after each question

GALLSTONES AND LIVER STONES SYMPTOM CHECKLIST

1) Do you have pain in the upper right abdomen?	
2) Do you have pain in the mid-right side of the back?	
3) Do you feel ill after eating fatty foods?	
4) Are you frequently nauseous?	
5) Have you lost your appetite?	
6) Are your stools light in color?	
7) Is there a yellowish color to your skin or eyes?	
Total	

PARASITE SYMPTOM CHECKLIST

1) Are you chronically tired even after several good nights' sleep?	
2) Have you had loose stools or diarrhea for more than two weeks?	
3) Do you grind your teeth or wake up frequently at night?	
4) Do you have mucus or blood in your stools?	
5) Is there undigested food in your stool?	
6) Do you experience frequent muscle and joint pain?	
7) Do you gravitate more and more toward high-sugar-content foods and	
Total	

SIBO CANDIDA IBS/GUT DYSBIOSIS SYMPTOM CHECKLIST

1) Do you experience frequent heart palpitations?	
2) Do you struggle to concentrate or experience frequent brain fog?	
3) Do you experience frequent abdominal pain, bloating, gas, diarrhea, or constipation?	
4) Do you have frequent prostatitis (men) or yeast infections (women)?	
5) Do you have psoriasis, eczema, dermatitis, or athlete's foot?	
6) Have you become sensitive to certain foods?	
7) Do you have dizzy spells, or has your eyesight deteriorated?	
8) Do you experience involuntary muscle twitching or facial tics?	
Total	

BURRIS GUT HEALTH CHECKLIST

Name_____Date of Birth_____Age____Sex_____Today's Date_____

NOT AT ALL	SOMEWHAT		MODERATELY	A LOT
1	———————————————	5	———————————————	10

Please write a score of 1-10 after each question

GALLSTONES AND LIVER STONES SYMPTOM CHECKLIST	
1) Do you have pain in the upper right abdomen?	
2) Do you have pain in the mid-right side of the back?	
3) Do you feel ill after eating fatty foods?	
4) Are you frequently nauseous?	
5) Have you lost your appetite?	
6) Are your stools light in color?	
7) Is there a yellowish color to your skin or eyes?	
Total	

PARASITE SYMPTOM CHECKLIST	
1) Are you chronically tired even after several good nights' sleep?	
2) Have you had loose stools or diarrhea for more than two weeks?	
3) Do you grind your teeth or wake up frequently at night?	
4) Do you have mucus or blood in your stools?	
5) Is there undigested food in your stool?	
6) Do you experience frequent muscle and joint pain?	
7) Do you gravitate more and more toward high-sugar-content foods and	
Total	

SIBO CANDIDA IBS/GUT DYSBIOSIS SYMPTOM CHECKLIST	
1) Do you experience frequent heart palpitations?	
2) Do you struggle to concentrate or experience frequent brain fog?	
3) Do you experience frequent abdominal pain, bloating, gas, diarrhea, or constipation?	
4) Do you have frequent prostatitis (men) or yeast infections (women)?	
5) Do you have psoriasis, eczema, dermatitis, or athlete's foot?	
6) Have you become sensitive to certain foods?	
7) Do you have dizzy spells, or has your eyesight deteriorated?	
8) Do you experience involuntary muscle twitching or facial tics?	
Total	

Food and Fitness Planner

Consistent control of your emotional state includes what you eat and drink and the type and amount of exercise you get. Why is it important to plan your food and fitness schedule? It is important because the process of an unconscious attack on the body with food, alcohol, or drugs can start a day or even days before you indulge in a behavior that will throw you completely off course and out of control. Planning your food and fitness schedule is a big part of reprogramming these behaviors; you need to plan them out until they become automatic.

Starting from the top, you have a start date and end date. You always want to plan your food and fitness schedule the day before, so on this first page, you start on Sunday and plan your food schedule for Monday. On Monday, you plan your schedule for Tuesday, and so on.

Food & Fitness Plan Instruction Set

Food Plan - Please plan your meals the day before. If you are working with a Registered Dietitian or Nutritionist, you will need to mark in estimates of the following along with the type of food. For a more comprehensive breakdown of the foods you eat, look up "Glycemic Index" on Google.

P – Grams of Protein

C - Grams of Carbohydrates

F - Grams of Fat

Total Oxalates: You must track and adjust your oxalate intake accordingly if you scored a 5 or above on any Gut Health Checklist questions. Low oxalate intake is considered to be less than 50 mg daily.

Carbs Glycemic Index: Weight loss is not about calories it is about insulin resistance. Therefore, if your objective is weight loss, you must closely monitor how quickly your food turns into sugar, stimulating the pancreas to produce insulin.

Water: Estimated amount of water

Alcohol: It is essential to be honest here as your mitochondria depend on it.

Sleep: Sleep is a fundamental issue when taking control of your emotional state and Food & Fitness plan. The body sees sleep deprivation as a state of stress, and cortisol is a stress hormone. Cortisol causes, in turn, the release of insulin.

Emotionally Driven Food: This is where you mark your emotionally driven food or drink. Identify the emotion and use the **Stop** and **Replace** System to initiate change and take control.

Fitness Plan: Please plan your fitness schedule the day before and mark down the type of workout and amount of time. If you did aerobics, only mark your approximate heart rate.

Medication: List all medications here. Some medications and supplements are incompatible, so tracking them is critical.

Supplements: List your supplements here. Always check with your MD before implementing any new supplements, especially if you are on any medications.

Weight: A recent study found that people most successful at maintaining a consistent weight weighed themselves daily. You must ultimately determine if this is going to work for you.

FOOD & FITNESS PLANNER

Start Date_____   End Date_____

MONDAY	TUESDAY	WEDNESDAY
Food Plan	**Food Plan**	**Food Plan**
Morning:	**Morning:**	**Morning:**
P		
C		
F		
Water:		
Afternoon:	**Afternoon:**	**Afternoon:**
P		
C		
F		
Water:		
Evening:	**Evening:**	**Evening:**
P		
C		
F		
Total Oxalates:		
Carbs Glycemic Index:		
Water:		
Alcohol:		
Sleep:		
Emotionally Driven Food	**Emotionally Driven Food**	**Emotionally Driven Food**
Fitness Plan	**Fitness Plan**	**Fitness Plan**
Medication:		
Supplements:		
Weight:	**Weight:**	**Weight:**

FOOD & FITNESS PLANNER

Start Date_____ End Date_____

THURSDAY	FRIDAY	SATURDAY
Food Plan	**Food Plan**	**Food Plan**
Morning:	**Morning:**	**Morning:**
P		
C		
F		
Water:		
Afternoon:	**Afternoon:**	**Afternoon:**
P		
C		
F		
Water:		
Evening:	**Evening:**	**Evening:**
P		
C		
F		
Total Oxalates:		
Carbs Glycemic Index:		
Water:		
Alcohol:		
Sleep:		
Emotionally Driven Food	**Emotionally Driven Food**	**Emotionally Driven Food**
Fitness Plan	**Fitness Plan**	**Fitness Plan**
Medication:		
Supplements:		
Weight:	**Weight:**	**Weight:**

FOOD & FITNESS PLANNER

Start Date _____ End Date _____

MONDAY	TUESDAY	WEDNESDAY
Food Plan	**Food Plan**	**Food Plan**
Morning:	**Morning:**	**Morning:**
P		
C		
F		
Water:		
Afternoon:	**Afternoon:**	**Afternoon:**
P		
C		
F		
Water:		
Evening:	**Evening:**	**Evening:**
P		
C		
F		
Total Oxalates:		
Carbs Glycemic Index:		
Water:		
Alcohol:		
Sleep:		
Emotionally Driven Food	**Emotionally Driven Food**	**Emotionally Driven Food**
Fitness Plan	**Fitness Plan**	**Fitness Plan**
Medication:		
Supplements:		
Weight:	**Weight:**	**Weight:**

FOOD & FITNESS PLANNER

Start Date_____ End Date_____

THURSDAY	FRIDAY	SATURDAY
Food Plan	**Food Plan**	**Food Plan**
Morning:	**Morning:**	**Morning:**
P		
C		
F		
Water:		
Afternoon:	**Afternoon:**	**Afternoon:**
P		
C		
F		
Water:		
Evening:	**Evening:**	**Evening:**
P		
C		
F		
Total Oxalates:		
Carbs Glycemic Index:		
Water:		
Alcohol:		
Sleep:		
Emotionally Driven Food	**Emotionally Driven Food**	**Emotionally Driven Food**
Fitness Plan	**Fitness Plan**	**Fitness Plan**
Medication:		
Supplements:		
Weight:	**Weight:**	**Weight:**

FOOD & FITNESS PLANNER

Start Date_____ End Date_____

MONDAY	TUESDAY	WEDNESDAY
Food Plan	**Food Plan**	**Food Plan**
Morning:	**Morning:**	**Morning:**
P		
C		
F		
Water:		
Afternoon:	**Afternoon:**	**Afternoon:**
P		
C		
F		
Water:		
Evening:	**Evening:**	**Evening:**
P		
C		
F		
Total Oxalates:		
Carbs Glycemic Index:		
Water:		
Alcohol:		
Sleep:		
Emotionally Driven Food	**Emotionally Driven Food**	**Emotionally Driven Food**
Fitness Plan	**Fitness Plan**	**Fitness Plan**
Medication:		
Supplements:		
Weight:	**Weight:**	**Weight:**

FOOD & FITNESS PLANNER

Start Date_____   End Date_____

THURSDAY	FRIDAY	SATURDAY
Food Plan	**Food Plan**	**Food Plan**
Morning:	**Morning:**	**Morning:**
P		
C		
F		
Water:		
Afternoon:	**Afternoon:**	**Afternoon:**
P		
C		
F		
Water:		
Evening:	**Evening:**	**Evening:**
P		
C		
F		
Total Oxalates:		
Carbs Glycemic Index:		
Water:		
Alcohol:		
Sleep:		
Emotionally Driven Food	**Emotionally Driven Food**	**Emotionally Driven Food**
Fitness Plan	**Fitness Plan**	**Fitness Plan**
Medication:		
Supplements:		
Weight:	**Weight:**	**Weight:**

FOOD & FITNESS PLANNER

Start Date_____ End Date_____

MONDAY	TUESDAY	WEDNESDAY
Food Plan	**Food Plan**	**Food Plan**
Morning:	**Morning:**	**Morning:**
P		
C		
F		
Water:		
Afternoon:	**Afternoon:**	**Afternoon:**
P		
C		
F		
Water:		
Evening:	**Evening:**	**Evening:**
P		
C		
F		
Total Oxalates:		
Carbs Glycemic Index:		
Water:		
Alcohol:		
Sleep:		
Emotionally Driven Food	**Emotionally Driven Food**	**Emotionally Driven Food**
Fitness Plan	**Fitness Plan**	**Fitness Plan**
Medication:		
Supplements:		
Weight:	**Weight:**	**Weight:**

FOOD & FITNESS PLANNER

Start Date _____ End Date _____

MONDAY	TUESDAY	WEDNESDAY
Food Plan	**Food Plan**	**Food Plan**
Morning:	**Morning:**	**Morning:**
P		
C		
F		
Water:		
Afternoon:	**Afternoon:**	**Afternoon:**
P		
C		
F		
Water:		
Evening:	**Evening:**	**Evening:**
P		
C		
F		
Total Oxalates:		
Carbs Glycemic Index:		
Water:		
Alcohol:		
Sleep:		
Emotionally Driven Food	**Emotionally Driven Food**	**Emotionally Driven Food**
Fitness Plan	**Fitness Plan**	**Fitness Plan**
Medication:		
Supplements:		
Weight:	**Weight:**	**Weight:**

THE TRANCE-FORMATION

Trance describes a subconscious state, or what you may refer to as meditation or prayer. It is a means of having a greater level of communication with the subconscious. The last half of this term, Formation, refers to the formation of information during your Trance or the structure of your self-talk and pictures. I also refer to the Trance-Formation as accelerated restructuring.

The most powerful means of changing your subconscious programming is through the use of light trance. The intention is for **you** to take control of your subconscious. The Trance-Formation is also important because it is, in essence, prayer or meditation with a purpose. It is designed to help you learn how to meditate and for those who already meditate to increase the power of your meditation or prayer substantially.

During your light trance, you remain aware of everything around you and in complete control, instead of being given generic or general information. The information used during your trance will be specific to you, as established in the first six steps of the program. The purpose of the Trance-Formation is not to quiet the mind as in most forms of meditation. The mind has a certain speed; it is going to run regardless of what you attempt because this is just part of being alive. You can, however, take control of what it is doing, and this is what the Trance-Formation is all about.

What you say to yourself is more important than anything anyone says to you or about you. Once you have learned the dialogue of the induction, you can use this to put yourself in a relaxed state that will allow you greater control over your subconscious processes. You must put yourself in a Light Trance at least once a day.

The effectiveness of your meditation will always be determined by what you say to yourself and the pictures you choose. The Trance-Formation requires that you are not involved in any activity. Before engaging in the Trance-Formation, select a quiet place where you can relax and fully connect with the process.

Following is the text for the Trance-Formation. You can use this to make an audio or edit it to suit your needs perfectly and then memorize it like a script to put yourself in a relaxed state that will, in essence, rearrange the furniture in your head.

The Trance-Formation Meditation

Find a comfortable spot, and we shall begin. First, establish a clear vision of what you want in and around your new self. When viewing this picture, make sure your body is exactly as you wish, you are with people you love, and you are in a location that makes you feel incredible. Fully associate with this image.

Once you have a clear vision of your new life, gently set it aside for a moment, and you will begin the process of the Trance-Formation Meditation.

Begin by placing your palms face up on your thighs. Now, place two swirling white lights in the center of your palms. Within the swirling lights, in your left palm, see the people or things that invoke your most powerful emotional state and with the most loving, wonderful energy. What are they doing?

In your right hand, place your current self inside the swirling light. As you watch the swirling patterns, you begin to notice that the person inside the light is changing, shifting, transforming, and becoming exactly the person you designed.

Now, take a deep breath in through your nose and slowly exhale through your mouth as you bring your palms up to your chest, and this swirling, white-loving light enters your chest. Take another deep breath in through your nose and slowly exhale out through your mouth as your eyelids become heavy and fall from their own weight.

With every breath, you become more and more relaxed as this white, loving light moves through the entire cavity of the chest, illuminating every cell and any dark areas of the body. This white-loving light continues to move up your neck and into your head, illuminating every cell of the brain while moving back down into your neck, down your shoulders into your arms, and out to the end of your fingertips. This loving white light continues to move down into your stomach cavity as you begin to see a set of stairs, ten steps to the bottom.

As you take the first step down these stairs, you go down a thousand steps and become more relaxed as this white, swirling light continues to move down into your legs, into your feet, and out through the ends of your toes.

As you purposefully take the second, third, and fourth steps, you continue to go down a thousand steps with each step, while this white light expands outward and completely encompasses you, illuminating every cell and destroying any dark areas of the consciousness and body. This, white, loving light becomes focused and concentrated on all of the areas of the body that may need to be healed and remains there until the problem is dissolved and replaced by new, healthy, illuminated cells.

Looking upward, you begin to see a clear image of your newly emerged self. You see yourself and the structure of the picture just as you described it in The Subconscious Self-Image. You are in a location that makes you feel incredible with all the people, colors, sounds, and aromas that you desire.

This picture is panoramic and fully encompasses your field of vision. You *make the choice to step into this picture and become fully associated with it.

As you begin to absorb all the good feelings of this picture, you search the boundaries and discover ways to make it even better every day.

The images that you see empower you. You can see yourself taking each step to get to this wonderful new version of yourself. You are making better choices, sleeping better at night, choosing foods that make you strong, and people who generate a profound synergy.

As you're looking through these images, keep the colors bright and vivid, just like your associated image, make sure you can hear the sounds and voices that helped you stay focused, and match the vibrancy of this image with the vibrancy of those swirling white lights.

Looking at these images, you begin to ask yourself the first two key questions:

1) Does this work for me?

2) How do I feel, and will I benefit from the results of this? (Remember that If the answer to

this is no, you will ask yourself the next key question.)

3) What can I use to replace this with that will benefit me?

You continue to reshape and change what you are doing and the contents of the picture until you get exactly what you want. Stop and Replace this picture any time you feel yourself drifting off course. You now gently step out of this image and come back to our staircase on the fourth step.

With your images fully integrated, you continue going down the stairs to the fifth, sixth, and seventh steps. You continue to go down a thousand steps with each step. This, white, loving light continues to swirl within you and around you, becoming the perfect magnet for everything you desire.

As you feel your vibrant images, other pictures begin to emerge. These are pictures of you going through your daily life: working, playing, and interacting with people and things. Some of these pictures may be of you rationalizing a poor choice or making a mistake, and you begin to reprimand yourself. You have the power to immediately recognize this and begin to ask yourself the next two key questions:

4) What can I learn from this? And

5) How can I use this experience to move more quickly toward my objectives?

If an answer does not come right away, continue to chant these questions until the mind can no longer reprimand.

Suddenly, the power of these and other Empowering Questions begins to work for you, and you will find that something that just seemed useless or even harmful has now become useful and empowering.

This, white, loving light continues to move through your body and expand outward. Your Mind, Body, and Spirit become fully connected. All of your objectives and the ways to accomplish them begin to come into clear view.

As other pictures come into view, there are some that feel intrusive. You immediately ask yourself: Does this image work for me? When the answer is no, you immediately say, **Stop** to yourself. This initiates your ability to halt this image and make the picture smaller and smaller, more and more unidentifiable, until it is a little black BB in front of your face, which you can destroy in a way that makes you smile. You can shoot it back behind you and blow it up into a billion molecules or smash it with a hammer, whatever you feel is the most effective.

You find yourself saying "**Replace**" to yourself while simultaneously bringing up your empowered image. You know you can initiate this process a thousand times a second if that is what it takes to destroy the old picture. You *fully* understand you are the one who now controls the subconscious. Feel your body as it shifts back into the powerful position evoked by your choice to focus on your associated images.

You continue to relax with every breath you take, and all the good feelings of the associated image envelope you. Concentrating on this picture, you continue to relax, feeling good about both images and still going deeper and deeper with every breath. While keeping your empowered image in view, you call upon another white, loving light that enters through the top of your head, moving down and adding to the already existing light. Feel the peace that comes from knowing you can invite this loving light any time you need.

Every night, as you go to bed, you may call upon this loving light and begin to create your own dialogue that will allow you to enter a subconscious state. This, loving, swirling light continues to enter the top of your head, moving down into your neck, your shoulders, down your arms, and out through the ends of your fingers, illuminating every cell along the way.

As you continue to go deeper and deeper, this loving light moves down into the chest and abdomen and into the legs and feet.

This light continues to pour down through the top of your head, filling every cell, and then it expands, completely surrounding you. As you become empowered by this powerful, white, loving light, you continue down the stairs to the eighth, ninth, and tenth steps.

You continue to go deeper and deeper as questions begin to enter your mind, Empowering Questions that will maintain and perpetuate your love, health, wealth, and self-image. Questions for your emotional and spiritual LOVE begin to emerge:

- What do I need to do to keep my love from turning into anxiety, negative self-talk, or anger?
- How can I continually and perpetually live in this light of love?
- How can I be more of a magnet for loving energy?
- What action do I need to take to realize the full potential of my emotional and spiritual love?
- How can I use my emotional and spiritual love to improve my communication skills?
- What do I need to do to perceive all past and current relationships as beneficial?
- What will happen today that will give me incredible pleasure for no reason?
- What questions do I need to ask myself to perpetuate a healthy emotional and spiritual love?

As this white, loving light continues to pour down through the top of your head and destroy any dark areas while illuminating every cell, Empowering Questions for your health begin to emerge while your subconscious continues to work on the questions for your love:

- How can I consistently maintain a 7, 8, or 9 regarding my overall health?
- What action must I take to maintain a consistent fitness program?
- What do I need to do to feel this good all the time?
- How can I make sure I stay in the habit of changing things that do not work for me?
- How can I maintain my excitement and enthusiasm for my fitness and diet program every day?
- What exercise do I enjoy enough to make a permanent part of my daily or weekly routine?
- How can I ensure I only ask questions that work for me and move me quickly toward my objectives?
- What emotional state do I need to change that may keep me from optimum health?
- How can I make sure my mind, body, and spirit are always fully integrated?
- What other questions do I need to ask that will keep me moving toward and perpetuate my desired health?

As your subconscious continues to work on the questions for your love and health, your wealth questions begin to emerge:

- What action do I need to take to initiate and perpetuate my desired wealth?
- What action do I need to take to maximize my productivity every day?
- What do I need to do to perceive every experience as a benefit?
- What do I need to do to become more of a magnet for everything I desire?
- How can I make all things in life work for me?
- How can I increase my decision-making speed?
- What other questions must I ask that will keep me moving toward my desired wealth?

As your love, health, and wealth questions continue, your self-image questions begin to emerge:

- How can I maintain the image of this positive perception every second, every minute, every hour of the day?
- What do I need to do to maintain my Objective Picture and the image of my new self?
- What can I add to this picture to help me maintain this new image?
- What do I need to do to feel fantastic all the time?
- What action do I need to take today that will make me feel great?
- What information do I need to perpetuate my love, health, wealth, and self-image?
- What questions do I need to ask myself every day that will ensure my emotional well-being?
- What information do I need to ensure the success of my objectives?

As you continue to ask yourself Empowering Questions, the white loving light begins to swirl at your feet as you start going back up the stairs to the ninth, eighth, seventh, and sixth steps. With every breath, you pull this energy up into your legs, abdomen, chest, arms, hands, neck, and head as you continue to walk back up the stairs to the fifth, fourth, third, and second steps.

As you step up to the first step and then the top of the stairs, your new vision of yourself becomes clearer than ever. Your body now becomes completely and fully energized, and as soon as you wish, you may come back with the knowledge that you are capable of creating the life you choose starting right now.

Be ye Transformed by the Renewing of Your Mind

MAINTENANCE

The program process of SR™ **immediately generates dramatic results** that are unseen in any other form of behavior change.

The big issue is maintenance after you have established your initial results. There are several variables as to whether an unwanted behavior will return, if ever. Age, gender, the amount of physical abuse, and how the behavior was learned to begin with are all factors. Let us start with age. Once past the age of 40, a behavior is going to be more difficult to restructure. Women seem to have about 10 to 15 years longer than men regarding their ability to restructure in a short period. In other words, men get stuck in a behavior at a much more dramatic level at a younger age. The success rate goes down for men over the age of 50 and women over the age of 60.

You can only move forward if your thinking remains flexible, and you become more inflexible as you age. If you understand and accept this, it will make the process of change easier.

You must follow up on yourself for a minimum of ninety days. After that, you will need to determine whether you are satisfied with your programming; if not, you must continue to restructure subconscious processes that do not work.

Another variable is how you learned the behavior. If there was physical abuse in conjunction with emotional and verbal abuse, this is going to require a greater level of maintenance at any age. When I compiled the first version of this program process in the late 1980s and put myself through it, the results were so dramatic I thought I had completely fixed myself. The reality was that after a few months, I had just peeled away a couple of surface layers to restructure the true core issues. During the first couple of years, I ran through the program about four times yearly. I now put myself through it twice a year. It is a wonderful thing to stay tuned up and in control.

The last and probably the most significant variable in maintaining control of your subconscious is that up until now, you have been programmed to allow the subconscious to run itself. Once you allow the subconscious to run itself again, you become subject to any and all information stored in the subconscious and new information you are continually exposed to.

You must program yourself to ask the five key questions every day. The first one is especially important because you can apply it to the two components that bring about an emotional state and behavior.

Ask Yourself Everyday

- What am I saying to myself right now?
- Is my internal dialogue empowering me?
- What pictures am I allowing in the subconscious?
- Are my internal pictures keeping me in my most powerful emotional state?

Working with an SR™ Practitioner

Working with an SR™ Practitioner is your best insurance for establishing and maintaining permanent behavior change. All SR™ Practitioners are trained to maximize your ability to restructure and maintain your new programming. SR™ Practitioners have a wide range of expertise, which includes Psychologists, Psychiatrists, former Army Rangers, Marines, Air Force, Registered Dietitians, Teachers, Counselors, Personal Trainers, and Registered Nurses. If you want to take this program process as far as it can go, you may want to work with an SR™ Practitioner.

Step 1 - The Emotional Checklist

If you do the program independently, you can make a free account at BurrisConnect.com, where Steps 1 and 6 enable you to measure and track your emotional and gut health.

After the first thirty days, your maintenance schedule for the Emotional Checklist needs to be once a month, and compare it to the one you filled out the previous month. Please keep in mind you can always do more. The only question is, how far do you want to take it?

Step 2 - The Subconscious Perspective

Are you happy with the progression of your objectives?

If the answer to this question is no, reevaluate your objectives. Do you need to upgrade them? If you upgrade them, make sure you respond to the other statements and questions from the Subconscious Perspective regarding your objectives.

Empowering Questions

Have all of your Empowering Questions from the Subconscious Perspective been answered?

If they have not, keep asking, and then make sure you write them down. If you have answered all of your questions, are you completely satisfied with the answers? If you are unsatisfied with the answers, restructure the questions until you are completely satisfied. Example: If one of your questions was…"How can I lose this weight?" You may need to enhance it by asking: "What action do I need to take every day to reach my objective weight and have fun doing it?"

Step 3 - Subconscious Self-Image

Have you been able to maintain your new self-image?

If you have not been able to maintain your new self-image, then this is definitely something you will want to work on in the Stop and Replace System. The issue at the top of the Stop and Replace System would be "Not Maintaining My New Self Image."

Step 4 - The Stop and Replace System

Are you completely happy with the results of the issues you have addressed in the Stop and Replace System?

If the answer to this is no, have you been reading this page every day? You must go back and reread the Stop and Replace System every day for at least a week. If you do not notice a difference, you need to go back and start a new page with better benefits, more powerful questions, and a more compelling replacement picture. Continue to restructure the issue you wish to change until you get what you want and have fully reprogrammed yourself.

Has anything else come up that you need to restructure?

Step 5 - The Heart of SR™

Have you picked out at least one question per category, and are you reading those questions aloud daily? This is the minimum you need to do every day for the rest of your life. The mind is an incredible multitasking machine, so you can ask as many questions as you wish, and it will work on them all.

Step 6 – Cracking the Gut Health Code

Do you understand all of the mechanisms outlined in Step 6, "Cracking the Gut Health Code?"

Cracking the Gut Health Code was designed to inform you and your MD about the latest science in gut health and how it affects the complex processes of the mind, so it is OK if you do not understand all of it as long as you go over it with your MD.

Have any foods been emotionally driven?

If the answer to this is yes, did you address the issue in the Stop and Replace System? If you have not, you must continue to restructure it until you have reprogrammed yourself.

Step 7 - The Trance-Formation

The most control you will ever assert over the subconscious is when you are in a subconscious state. This is why you must use the Trance-Formation until you have established your method of putting yourself in a subconscious state at least once daily.

Your Support System

Once you establish the foundation for reprogramming yourself, it is up to you to implement these tools anytime you discover something that does not work. A client once commented that her mind was running amuck a few months after going through the program. I asked her if she attempted to Stop and Replace the process, and the answer was no. As I stated earlier, the subconscious will run itself if you do not run the subconscious. You can hire an SR™ Practitioner to implement, develop, and grow your support system if you belong to any group. Here again, the fundamental question is. What is going to work the best for me?

☆ ☆ ☆ ☆ ☆

If you found this book helpful, please consider leaving a review at Amazon or GoodReads to help others.

www.BurrisInstitute.com

www.BurrisConnect.com

Made in the USA
Middletown, DE
07 July 2024

56986599R00097